Sex Tips for Dogs

CW00551822

Sex Tips for Dogs

Randy Barker

*the world's foremost authority
on canine sexual politics*

(Owned and trained by Angela Patmore)

Stanley Paul
London Sydney Auckland Johannesburg

Stanley Paul & Co. Ltd

An imprint of Century Hutchinson

Brookmount House, 62–65 Chandos Place
Covent Garden, London WC2N 4NW

Century Hutchinson Australia (Pty) Ltd
88–91 Albion Street, Surry Hills, NSW 2010

Century Hutchinson New Zealand Limited
191 Archers Road, PO Box 40–086, Glenfield, Auckland 10

Century Hutchinson South Africa (Pty) Ltd
PO Box 337, Bergvlei 2012, South Africa

First published 1988

Set in 11/12½pt Linotron Century
by Input Typesetting Ltd, London

Printed and bound in Great Britain
by Anchor Brendon Ltd, Tiptree, Essex

British Library Cataloguing in Publication Data

Patmore, Angela
  Sex tips for dogs.
  1. Pets: Dogs. Humour
  I. Title
  636. 7′00207

ISBN 0 09 173717 6

Contents

Our Mounting Problem

Brother dogs, we're up against it!

We've been trodden underfoot by the Human Occupation of this planet. We've let ourselves be bought and sold and chained up without sticking out for our proper rights. Instead of serving Nature, we've been mucking about serving Man, the Bringer of the Bowl. He has whipped and whacked us continually for many thousands of years. We have been beaten and broken! We have been chemically and surgically interfered with in our gonad areas! What's more, we've been prevented from freely choosing our own mates and leading normal sex lives. Oh yes. *And* palmed off with bitches of dubious genetic quality. A lot of them look like something out of a reptile house, or a laboratory. And these so-called 'Pedigrees' have been cloned by humans in order to insult us and ruin our race. Dogs like myself, that are free of this inbreeding, and who look like canines as Nature intended us to be, are referred to with utter contempt, as 'Mongrels', 'Crossbreeds', 'Heinzes', Bitzers', and 'Mixed Jobs'. Bloody cheek. Neutered and nobbled, we are! Sent to the doggie dustbins called 'dogs' homes' and put down by the hundred thousand.

Look around. What do you notice, in this day and age? 'No dogs allowed'. Am I making this up? 'Keep dogs off grassed areas'. 'No dogs in this pub'. Shops, playgrounds, parks, beaches – we've been banned from the lot. Prevented even from going from where we went before in search of decent mates. The Chinese have wiped us out in Peking. (They've eaten most of us over there.) The Icelanders have kicked us out of Reykjavik. We're getting the bums' rush, from New York to Walthamstow. And it won't end there. This species of garmented goofs means to do for us, once and for all. The anti-dog-poo brigade are after us now with pooper scoopers. It'll be guns next. Dogs all over the world are coming up to me and saying, 'Randy Barker, we are desperate! Our minds are mush. Our glands are on the turn. Our genes are up the spout and down the chute. Can't you do something to HELP us?' It breaks my heart,

Brothers and Brigands, to hear them PLEADING with me to take up the leadership, offering me their best bones to pour my genius into the fight. Well, all right, I said. I'll do it. But only if I'm obeyed at all times.

What can we do? We can act now, before it's too late. We must face the facts of life. We must go forth and multiply, until we outnumber humans and have our paws on the power. We must tackle our Mounting Problem, while we still have the tackle to tackle it with. And this book, fellow Four-legs, tells how!

What you are about to read is actually a series of lectures on dog sexuality, delivered by me personally (as the world's foremost authority on canine sexual politics), under the most difficult and dangerous circumstances, at dead of night in a makeshift lecture theatre in a highly secret location, behind the brickyard at the back of the Dog and Duck in East London, England. The manuscripts were afterwards conveyed to the publishers a sheet at a time in the mouths of two of my loyal followers, who risked being picked up and flung in Battersea Dogs' Home. The lectures were taken down verbatim, so readers should excuse any sordidness. In the interests of historical accuracy, outbursts from the floor have not been edited out. The live audience – well, most of them were alive when we started – consisted of a band of dog brigands and freebooters who had sworn beforehand to die for the cause, and to accompany me on rallies throughout the country, throughout the world, throughout the universe, spreading the bark on dog revolt and sexual litteration.

This is the Dog Bible. Read it, and be prepared to Bite for what is Right!

RANDY BARKER,
behind the Dog and Duck,
May 1988

They've wiped us out in Peking

Chapter One

Some Vital Statistics

Good evening, Brothers and Brigands – don't answer back. Could one of you jump up and push the light switch on with his nose? Thank you.

It is now 10 p.m. Canine Mean Time, and we are gathered here, in this highly secret location behind the brickyard at the back of the Dog and Duck, to expound a new philosophy, quite unlike any you have ever heard before. Because of the tremendous danger and difficulty of trying to find a venue for future lectures, I intend to deliver my series of talks in their entirety tonight. At dawn, armed in the knowledge I am about to give you, we will march forth onto the streets to begin the Canine Uprising. Anyone attempting to disrupt this meeting will be severely punished and, if necessary, ejected by the Henchdogs you see here about me. Is that clear? Good. Off we go, then.

Four thousand, six hundred and eighty-four million

Four thousand, six hundred and eighty-four million. That is a vital statistic to put a burble in your belly. That is a figure to send pups and bitches of a nervous disposition scuttling in the streets. You know why? Because 4,684,000,000 is the number of human beings currently infesting this planet. Well, 'currently'. The last survey was done four years ago, so at the rate they reproduce, they could have doubled that by now. I think there were two of them originally. Two nude sex maniacs who lived the life of Reilly in a garden with a big snake. How many do you suppose there are in the United Kingdom? 56,763,000 of them. Fast breeding and reacting. What about the United States? 240,468,000. China? 1,008,175,000. All on bicycles and rickshaws. WHY ARE THERE SO MANY OF THEM? It's because they've all made a life-long, in-depth study of SEX. From the cradle up, they're learning about Private

Parts, Organs, Bottoms and Boobs. Their whole lives depend on the subject. In fact, they attribute the original formation of the Universe to Sex. They speak about it with reverence, calling it The Big Bang. By this they mean the start of their population explosion, but I think there may be a naughty reference in there as well, if you follow. In any case, their entire culture is founded upon copulation. They do it at all ages, in all climes and in all countries, and they do it with anybody they can lay their hands on, as many times as humanly possible. Now and then, they take a breather. And do you know what they talk about on these occasions? The Dog Population Problem.

The Dog Population Problem

They don't know exactly how many dogs there are in this world, but however many it is, according to our Two-legged tormentors, it should be half that. One of them has estimated that there may be 150 million Mongrels (i.e. proper dogs) globally. Shock, horror, sharp intake of breath. Far too many! Dirty little devils! Exterminate the lot! In the United States there are between 50 and 80 million, so they're rounding us up and sticking us in decompression chambers. In Britain, where I have the misfortune to rake the streets, we run on a skeleton staff of six million dog souls. We don't have any seats in Parliament, and a lot of us don't have any seats at all and have to sit on the floor, but we're not complaining about that. We're worried about the 200,000 who get the chop every year.

YORKSHIRE TERRIERS: *'Pork chop! Pork chop! Oop the shop fort'*
Pork chop!'

Be quiet. So all this is taking its toll on dog sanity. Increasingly, in Britain and America, canine patients with 'severe management problems' are being taken regularly to animal behaviour clinics, dog hypnotists and pet psychiatrists, where aggression and anxiety are dealt with on an epidemic scale! Let me recreate for you a typical interview at one of these treatment centres.

As many times as humanly possible

Typical scene at dog psychiatric clinic

DR I. MESMER-MUTLEY (Animal behaviourist, Los Angeles):   What's the problem, Mrs Bingo?

MRS BINGO (dog owner): Well, he went for my husband's behind Sunday evening and hung onto his trousers, Doctor.

DR MESMER-MUTLEY: Dear oh dear, we can't have that, can we – what's his name again?

MRS BINGO: Bungo, Doctor.

DR MESMER-MUTLEY: We can't have that, can we, Bungo old chap?

BUNGO (sotto voce): Grrrr.

DR MESMER-MUTLEY: Now, I'm putting this towel on the floor, Mrs Bingo, and in a moment I'm going to blow this very high-pitched whistle and signal with my hand, thus. When you see the signal, I want you to lead Bungo, calmly but firmly, over to the towel, order him to sit, and give him one of these Chewy Choccy Dogdrops. Ready? Right. I'm blowing the high-pitched whistle and signalling – now! Mrs Bungo – lead Bingo over, calmly but firmly – now, tell him to sit: *Sit*, Mrs Bingo – no not you, the dog.

MRS BINGO: Good boy, Bungo, sit. No, *sit*!

DR MESMER-MUTLEY: *Sit*, Bungo!

MRS BINGO: *Sit*! Bad dog. Will you sit your arse down! (*A tussle ensues.*)

DR MESMER-MUTLEY: Hold him down, Mrs Bungo – Bingo – now, quick! Present the Chewy Choccy Dogdrop. No, here – give it to me!

BUNGO: Grrrrrrr.

MRS BINGO: He'll have you, Doctor.

DR MESMER-MUTLEY: Here, Bingo Bungo, have this Chewy –

BUNGO: Grrrr – *chomp, chomp!*

MRS BINGO: Sorry about that, Doctor, but I did warn you. He's a bit upset.

DR MESMER-MUTLEY: What the devil's the matter with the damn dog, anyway?

MRS BINGO: I don't know, Doctor. I think he's bonkers. Should I have him put down?

Little does it occur to anyone to ask poor Bungo what might be troubling him, or why he is so agitated. Could it not be because hundreds of thousands of his fellow creatures are being fried and frizzified in electric boxes, or zonked to death in decompression chambers without benefit of clergy? Could it not be that he regards schemes to exterminate his race, and bans to prevent him from going about his business, as an encroachment on his personal felicity? Might it not disturb him slightly to think that a group calling itself EDEN– Exterminate Dogs Everywhere Now – achieved the dignity of a national campaign, with MPs and VIPs acting as spokespersons? Or that another group calling itself LICC – the League for the Introduction of Canine Controls – is arguing for the withdrawal of all his tiny privileges? And worse than all this, worse even than the whippings and whackings and wipings-out which he has suffered from time immemorial at the hands of his Two-legged Tormentor – is Bungo not kept, for fifty-two weeks of every year, in a state of almost *permanent sexual frustration*, so that his eyes are standing out of his head like organ-stops? Small wonder, considering all this, that Bungo is *not* rowing with both oars in the water! It's a miracle of nature that he can function at all.

Sex and the single dog

I could tell you of many tragic cases, here in my own neighbourhood, of dogs who are so strung out by their ungratified urges that they have committed acts of violence against their own persons. No doubt you will know of similar cases in your own area, tormented dogs who have been driven by sexual longings to assault and battery, petty larceny, bizarre grimacing, drooling in the streets, fraud, murder and pulling big lumps out of their own coats. I know of one particular case – let us call him 'Cross Patch' to protect his identity – who is in such a turmoil over his sexual drives that if he went to see a psychiatrist, the psychiatrist would have to see a psychiatrist. Poor 'Cross' is so uptight that if the phone rings, he attacks people in the room. If the bathroom door is left open, he tries to get his head down the toilet. He has jumped from moving vehicles and upstairs windows – on one occasion without bothering to check if the window was open. He runs up and down the staircase of his house for three or four hours at a time and then defecates on the duvet. He has attempted to have sex with human legs, cushions, a sofa, a laundry bag, the family cat and, on 5 November last year, a Guy in a wheelbarrow. He is now very ill with windpipe collapse, after dragging on his lead for over an hour in heavy traffic having seen a bitch in a passing car. He has been whacked like a carpet, drugged like a junkie, locked up like a common criminal, and threatened many times with the chop, a big stick, pulverization and gonad-removal. Tragic? I'll say it's bloody tragic. But for every 'Cross Patch' in my locality, there are thousands, perhaps millions, just like him, out there in the wilderness. Some have been neutered (see my coming best-seller, *The Canine Eunuch*), and spend the rest of their lives writing poetry and staring out of the window. 'We look before and after, And pine for what is not.' Some may even be here tonight. I hope they will all, like brothers of one inward fire, join with us in the Revolution. *'For it will come, brothers, oh yea, it will come!'* 'Alleluya – Give a dog a bone!' (See the *Dog Hymnal*, No. 35.)

DOG BRIGANDS: *'Alleluya, brother!'*

Six million British dogs. A pathetic figure. A catastrophically inadequate figure, if we are going to come to power in the foreseeable future. Yes, I know it's difficult. But think of this: if every one of us took his or her procreational duties seriously, in one year we could have 3 million bitches mated twice, with two litters each of, say, ten pups – that's 3 million times two times ten – 60 million pups, plus the original adult population – 66 *million dogs* in the UK inside a twelvemonth. Which would mean that, within a year, we would actually outnumber the humans on these islands.

Now, why is this not done? Well, we all know why not, don't we? It's because human beings, when they are not busy blowing each other up, are destroying and neutering the dog population, and when they are not doing that, they are copulating, and when they are not copulating, they are seeing to it that we don't. Am I right?

(Cries of 'Yea, Alleluya!')

Good. *You.* No, you at the front, the Spaniel. Yes, you. Go and fetch my plastic waterbowl out of the yard, and put some water in it. You'll see a big pool out there full up with rainwater. Do you know how to fill a vessel? You take it in your teeth and pull it through the water, holding it the right way up. Then you come back and put it in front of me. Got that? Good – off you go.

Now then. Let me ask you a question. When was the last time you got lucky? Think carefully before you answer. If you're a particularly stupid dog like, say, a Yorkshire Terrier for example –

YORKSHIRE TERRIERS: *'Ere! Watch theeseln!'*

– you may have to get a proper dog to help you on this one. Now, think carefully. Rack your brains. When was the last time you had sex? Not sex with cushions – real sex, with a member of the opposite gender of the dog race? Can you recall it? Some of you may have been chemically or surgically attended to, but think back. Try to remember – it's important. Right. Got it? You've got a clear picture of that wondrous event in your minds, have you? Good. Now, I'm going to ask you a second question. What happened next? The chances are, it all went something like this (and although there are of course no bitches among the Brothers and Brigands here tonight, I include them here for the purposes of illustration):

Female Pedigree

I was taken in a crate/car to a strange place.

I was dragged into a shed.

An oddly familiar, snotty-looking, bug-eyed and very unattractive male was led in.

I was muzzled with a bandage and held firmly by the two human owners.

I was raped.

The humans had a cigarette, and a tidy sum changed hands.

I found out later that the male was my father/brother/grandfather.

Female Mongrel

I was sprayed with a chemical to mask my scent, and locked in the backyard behind a six-foot fence, yapping my head off for two weeks.

One day, after much suffering, a brave dog came to my rescue.

He tunnelled under the fence, but finding his way barred by wire netting, he summoned all his strength and leaped over the six-foot palings.

He was a magnificent Mongrel.

We mated.

My owner came out and gave us a good hiding.

I was shut in the cupboard for the rest of my season, having been given a 'morning after' injection at the vet's.

Male Pedigree (stud)

I was taken to that blessed shed again.

There was another bitch waiting.

She looked vaguely familiar, but then don't they all?

I did my duty.

I went outside for a bowl of water and read the *Telegraph Pole*.

This job gets on my —— nerves.

Male Mongrel

After weeks of fruitlessly roaming the streets, I sensed a bitch on heat in the neighbourhood.

Arriving at the property, I did a quick recce and found the bitch was locked up behind a six-foot fence in the backyard.

I fought my way to the front of the queue, maiming a spaniel cross and getting bitten in the chest.

I camped outside for days, without food or water, hardly daring to take my eyes off the fence and dodging two buckets of suds from an upstairs window.

Tunnelling down, and being prevented from access by wire netting, I summoned all my strength and leaped over the palings.

She was a magnificent, beautiful Mongrel bitch.

We mated.

Her owner came out and gave us a whacking, driving me off.

I arrived home. The front door flew open. My owner shouted, 'Where the —— hell have you been!' I got another hiding.

And these were the lucky ones! The ones still intact in their personal parts! The ones with randy regions not yet removed! The ones not forced to wear canine panties and chastity girdles with little belts and braces available from pet stores. Embarrassing? I'll say it's bloody embarrassing. They're trying to shame us into submission, and turn us into garmented goofs like themselves. They're trying to wreck our confidence and make us all depraved and weird like they are. Are we going to put up with it, Brothers and Brigands? Are we going to continue to act like the daft dogs they think we are?

(Cries of 'No! Bite the buggers! Rampage in the streets!')

Ah! 'The Bringer of the Bowl'. Very good. Put it down. No – there. *There.* Good dog. Sit.

As you can see from my schema of dog love lives (on page 15), there is an awful lot of difference between the sexual opportunities of a Mongrel and a Pedigree. Now, some of you may be a bit puzzled about this. Some of you may not even know what is meant by Mongrel and Pedigree. So let me explain. Otherwise, when we come to the nitty gritty Sex Tips, some of you will be all ends upward about doing whatever with whatever to whomever.

Manmade matings

The basic difference between a Pedigree and a Mongrel is this. The former is exploited for profit by man, and forced to mate with creatures man has invented, to produce Frankensteinian offspring he can flog at fashionable prices. The latter, wherever possible, is prevented from mating at all. All Mongrel matings are 'accidental' and much frowned upon by man as mere love matches between dogs which don't make them any money. I am a Mongrel. As a young nipper I was given away. My litter mates perished in a box weighted with stones and thrown in the duck pond. Mongrels are wonderful dogs – every one of us an individual, designed by Mother Nature's magic hand. Mongrel matings are the *only* ones of which she approves, which is why she blights poor inbred Pedigrees with diseases and deformities. It is not their fault. We're all brothers under the skin, and I fervently hope that every Pedigree listening to this message will join with us in the coming Revolution. But it must be said that Pedigrees are *manmade* dogs, and Mongrels are Natural dogs. And the reason why our whole race is the laughing stock of the animal kingdom is that Pedigrees have allowed man to poke his nose into their affairs. The Pedigree business is at the very heart of all our Mounting Problems.

Garmented goofs like themselves

Sex between Mongrels is natural. Our offspring promote the welfare of the species because our pups have 'hybrid vigour' – a technical term for the hardihood that enables us to survive and flaunt ourselves in the faces of the human breeders. How did *they* get in on the act anyway? What business was it of theirs where a dog got his leg over, or who had hot boots for whom? You'd think they'd mind their own business, seeing the state of some of their Two-legged types, wouldn't you?

Pedigrees were originally bred and designed by humans for particular jobs: hunting jobs, sniffing jobs, guarding jobs, war work, rescue work, millwheel and spit-turning work, baiting, fighting and murdering work. When humans trained a group of dogs to round up sheep, they found that by interbreeding these particular shepherdy dogs, pups could be produced that already had a rudimentary knowledge of the job. Over generations, the talent became more or less fixed. This saved the humans the bother of training every pup from scratch – so you see how the breeding lark got started. It was a labour-saving device. Now, when most of the dog jobs disappeared during the Industrial Revolution, and the fighting pits were banned, all these Pedigree workers were suddenly redundant. The human owners had a lot of bone-idle dogs on their hands, all bred into peculiar shapes and sizes. Little crooked short-legged ones for poking into holes after rats and foxes. Great big ones for battling in human wars. Squash-faced ones for baiting bulls and hanging on regardless of bloody noses. Man scratched his bonce and said to himself, 'Now, what can we do with all these weirdo dogs that cost so much to feed? How can they be turned to profit? I know. We'll have competitions to see who can produce the skinniest, the biggest, the smallest, the hairiest and the most sausage-like. Then we can sell the useless little devils and make a handsome living at it!' And that is what he did.

Show fever brought with it breed battiness. The Bulldog with the biggest head and the most smashed-in features won a prize. Never mind that he hadn't baited any bulls, or that he might need an operation to enable him to breathe: he was the champion. The Chihuahua with the most sticky-out eyeballs and the strangest little cranium won a prize, even if it was too small and dense to breed properly. Over generations, they became more and more exaggerated – the dwarves, the midgets, the pug-faces, the giants. Canine freaks. And the weirder they were, the better humans seemed to like them. And the higher the prices they were prepared to pay for them. And the more incentive they had to breed from them to produce thousands more *equally* freakish puppies, to sell for even higher prices – and so it goes on. 'Oh, this breed dates back to the time of the Ancient Megalomanians. They were used to pull royal carts with their teeth, and had to walk backwards, which is why they have those protruding dental

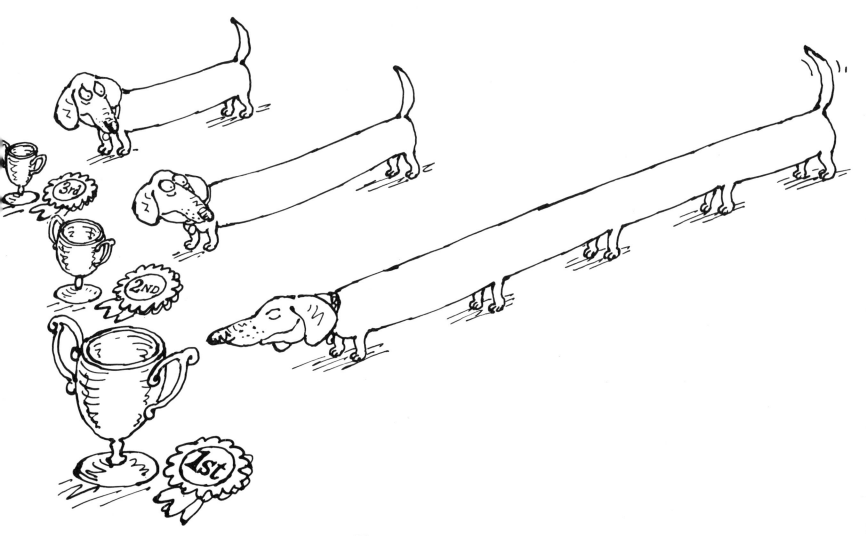

The most sausage-like

arrangements and front legs twelve inches shorter than their back legs. Pretty, aren't they? Give me £1,500 for the pair of them and I'll throw in a non-kick-over water bowl and a packet of Purepup yummie granules, which they've been raised on for generations!' And all the time, the poor devils have been bred from us Mongrels, as you can see from the ancient dog fossils in museums, some of them 12,000 years old.

You on the end – you look about 12,000 years old. What's your name?

BLOODHOUND: *'Bartleby, sir. I'm named after a character in one of Herman Melville's novels called "poor Bartleby" because his life is totally meaningless, sir.'*

Why is your head all baggy like that, Bartleby?

BLOODHOUND: *'Because I'm a Bloodhound. It's my breed standard, sir.'*

It's your breed standard. Come up here and show the audience your breed standard. Right. Now, do you see this? Look at this dog's head. Can you see where you're going, Bartleby?

BLOODHOUND: *'Not if I bend forward, sir. But I have a terrific sense of smell. Would you like to see me smell?'*

Do you have a job, Bartleby?

BLOODHOUND: *'No, sir.'*

Why is that?

BLOODHOUND: *'I applied to sniff for the Army, the police and the Royal Air Force police, who train drug-detection dogs for Customs and Excise and so on, but they all said Bloodhounds were unruly and our eyes were dust-traps.'*

And how long do you expect to live, Bartleby?

BLOODHOUND: *'Not long, sir. We big dogs don't live for very long.'*

So you can't see where you're going, you can't get a job, you haven't got long to live, you look like nothing on earth, and you owe all this to human breeders?

BLOODHOUND: *'Yes, sir.'*

Thank you, Bartleby. You can go and sit down. So what's to be done about Poor Bartleby, Brothers and Brigands?

POODLE: *'Should he be put down, sir?'*

No, of *course* he shouldn't be put down! Bartleby is not just Bartleby. Bartleby is a sign and symbol of what is wrong with dogdom in this day and age! Bartleby is what you get when you allow human beings to interfere with your sex lives! And what should be done about it? I'll tell you what should be done. From now on, dogs are not going to be bred by human beings! From now on, dogs are going to be bred by DOGS! How is this going to be achieved? Through Sex, Brothers and Brigands. Through Sex, Sex and more Sex! We are all, Mongrels *and* Pedigrees, going to get out on the streets, and we are going to mate with bitches of *our* choosing! And when we've mated with *those* bitches, we are going to go off and mate with *more* bitches, and yet *more* bitches, until we have peopled the world with pups who look like pups, pups as Nature intended them to be! And what are we going to do if humans try to stop us?

DOG BRIGANDS: *'Bite the Good Bite! Bite the Good Bite!'*

Bite the good bite. Here endeth the first lecture.

BORDER COLLIE: *'What about the rude bits, sir?'*

I'm coming to that.

Chapter Two

Understanding your Urges

A dog's body is a wonderful thing, but it is very complicated. Many dogs, when they look at themselves in a mirror, are thrown into confusion. What they felt sure was their right side turns out to be their left side; their left ear turns out to be their right ear, and everything, to the untrained eye, appears suddenly the wrong way round and quite different from what they imagined. The tail, which is a very conspicuous feature unless a dog has had it chopped off by a breeder, is scarcely visible in the mirror reflection, and a dog has to crane his neck to catch a glimpse of it twitching and wiggling in the background. Even more puzzling is the fact that one's rear parts are not visible at all, and many youngsters are frightened by this and become neurotic. In some breeds, it may be possible to twist right round to bring the backside into focus, though this is much more difficult in the case of short-necked dogs, and in any event, the private parts which make up the undercarriage and landing gear remain tantalizingly obscure. A dog therefore goes away from the mirror anxious and bewildered, wondering if his physical attributes conform to those of other members of his species.

Many young dogs write to me for advice, enclosing a stamped addressed envelope, asking about organs, prepuces and so on. I am usually able to reassure them, except in the case of particularly hairy breeds whose privates have never actually been seen, and pedigrees with a design fault which involves having one gonad not properly descended or, in extreme cases, neither. These dogs cannot be admitted to the show ring for fear of offending the delicate feelings of the Kennel Club, but worse, they are liable to be put down by their breeder if he or she detects this shortcoming. So I generally recommend these dogs to walk about with their hind legs crossed as much as possible, and suggest they avoid calling attention to their personal parts, for example by pointing or gesturing, or by cocking their legs against the tyres of the breeder's Land-Rover. The technical term for such animals is 'monorchid' if they have one ball descended, and 'cryptorchid' if their flower arrangement is even more mysterious.

The study of dogs' bodies is called 'anatomy'. The study of bitches' bodies is called 'lechery'. They are both sciences in their own right but one looks *in*, at the particulars of one's physique, and the other looks *out*, at the prospects for applying them successfully. In, out, in, out, shake it all about. The science of anatomy is not easy to explain to any dog who lacks a thorough grounding in the subject, but I can give you a lay dog's guide.

If you imagine your body cut in half lengthwise from head to tail, you may find it a bit upsetting, but try to picture a cross-section with one hind leg and half a bottom, and this will illustrate how the body's organs are distributed. Beneath the base of the tail, first of all, we have the *rectum*. Anything to do with rectums is 'rectumnal' and comes under the heading of 'toilet areas'. Travelling inwards we come to the *pelvis*, as in 'Elvis the Pelvis', who had a hit song that went 'You ain't nothing but a hound dog'. Within the pelvic structure we have, in male dogs, a little gland called the *prostate*, with a lot of important fluids inside. Sometimes, in middle-aged dogs, this gland becomes swollen and is known as an 'enlarged prostate'. Normally it secretes fluids into the system. A lot of dogs get confused over the prostate, and write to me asking if 'having a prostate problem' is the same as being shagged out. Well, it's a similar sort of thing. The prostate discharges chemicals into the *bladder*, which makes many dogs think that sex and urination are vaguely similar. They are not. The bladder is the organ for manufacturing writing ink and transmitting messages in pee code. It receives waste liquids from the kidneys and converts them by a chemical process, with the *ureter* and *vas deferens* in there as well, and the music goes round and round and comes out here. Yes, the Fox Terrier at the back?

FOX TERRIER: *'What is "vas deferens"?'*

Well, they're very small in some breeds. They're absolutely minute, in fact – so small that you can hardly see them.

BORDER COLLIE: *'A vas is a vessel, tube or duct carrying liquid.'*

Exactly – he's got it: a *vas* is a duct, hence 'vas deferens', a duct carrying different liquids, which in the dog happen to be very small tiddly bits rather like tadpoles, and hence *vasectomy*, cutting of the ducts. Now what is it?

FOX TERRIER: *'We had a duck once, in a pond in one of our villages in Bucks, but we had to share it between twelve of us before the whipper-in got us away. We ate the feathers and everything, except for our head hound Landsman who had one feather still sticking out of his mouth and got a good hiding.'*

Transmitting messages in pee code

CORGI: *'My owner had an Aylesbury duck in the back garden. She dug a hole in the lawn and sunk a plastic bowl in it and the duck used to sit in there wiggling its wings, happy as Larry, with the –'*

Shut up. Travelling down from the rectum, we come to the *testicles, epididymis, urethra, scrotum, penis* and *sheath.*

(Tittering breaks out.)

And that is the male urogenital system. Now we come on to the *urges* which this system generates, and which cause a dog so many problems. Yes?

COCKER SPANIEL: *'What about those other bits?'*

What other bits?

COCKER SPANIEL: *'Didymuses.'*

(Sounds of suppressed mirth.)

They're parts of the canine urogenital system. Vital parts. Absolutely vital.

COCKER SPANIEL: *'You don't know, do you?'*

Be quiet. Most of you will know the rudimentary –

COCKER SPANIEL: *'He doesn't know.'*

Right, that's it. Out! The lot of you. Go on. At risk to life and limb I came here. Concerned about the plight of our dog race plunging into oblivion. Get out – sling your hooks. You don't want to listen to my wisdom and experience and years of study, no, you know it all. You know how to get your legs over. Go on. Off you go.

(The dog brigands remain seated.)

So that's it, is it?

(Randy Barker collects up his papers and goes out.)

* * *

(Ten minutes later the door opens. It is Randy Barker again, with his papers. He places them on his lectern and carries on with his text.)

Most of you will have a rudimentary knowledge of what your bodies are for. When we are puppies, we learn to mount things, holding them firmly with our forelegs to stop them running away. If the object is living as for example, the leg of a human visitor, or next door's cat, it will frequently put up a struggle to escape, and as small pups we may easily be dislodged and thrown off on the floor with a violent flick. This traumatic experience often leads to puppies becoming despondent and lackadaisical about their sexual drives. Many turn to substitute hobbies, such as barking, muckspreading, or gnawing the piano legs. Others become so inhibited about trying to mate with living things that they redirect their energies towards inanimate objects. Sadly, many grown dogs fail to develop beyond this stage and, in psychoanalytical terms, become what we call 'arrested' – especially if their chosen sex objects happen to be pushchairs, fur coats or policemen's helmets. Few such dogs ever achieve a satisfactory union with a bitch, and we can all point to one or two pathetic cases and say, 'Look at that pervert – I'm glad I'm not like that dirty old weirdie dog!' But really, they are to be pitied: the dog who pokes his nose into airing cupboards, looking for piles of linen which he can squash into suitable shapes; the dog who sneaks towards his owner's armchair and seizes a cushion in his teeth for his fornicating purposes; the dog who follows coalmen on their delivery rounds, eyeing the sacks with a lovelorn expression – we have all seen them, furtively plying their trade and hoping not to be reported to the local authority. I once knew a German Shepherd whose owner had a motorbike, which he kept in a garage while he was working. The German Shepherd, whose name I won't mention because he lives not very far from here, at number 52, found that by standing on his hind legs in the garage, he could adjust himself to the seat of the motorbike, which was covered in black leather padding, and achieve an interesting relationship with the machine by jogging up and down. Afterwards, he would lie down beside the bike and go to sleep. One night his owner was on his way home from work when he caught sight of his motorbike running down the road with the terrified dog hanging on the pillion, after they had burst through the garage doors in cybernetic bliss. And then there was the Labrador who pushed into his local launderette and was in the midst of a pseudo-religious experience with a navy-blue washbag when an irate housewife emptied a bowl of suds over him. All these tragic and bewildered dogs are, in their various ways, desperately trying to obey their normal and natural urges, though you can't help wondering what gets into their filthy little minds. Warped by adolescent disappointments and longings, they have somehow forgotten what their wonderful dog bodies are for.

As, for example, the leg of a human visitor

Most dogs, if they have a sexual problem, naturally assume that human beings must be the cause of it, and they can usually name a particular individual who is responsible for their plight. Often, the blame is attributed to Margaret Thatcher or Ronald Reagan, with Ken Livingstone a popular choice in the Greater London area. But not *all* canine deviation is due to human kind.

(Cries of 'Rubbish! Maggie Maggie Maggie, woof woof woof!')

Occasionally – Silence! – occasionally, confusion arises in adolescence when a growing youngster is rebuffed in his tentative gropings by a bitch of ferocious temperament. (*'Mag–'*) WILL YOU SHUT UP! Or a bitch who has been fed exclusively on liver, and who breaks wind in his face. From such shocking beginnings, many an ambivalent trait develops. Again, confusion may arise even earlier, in the very litter, if all pups in the nest are of the male gender. The disappointed puppies, floundering among their litter mates in search of warm little female forms and finding only newspaper, bedroom slippers, the cat, a dead gerbil, and other males, are apt to assume this is a blueprint of the world at large. And at this very delicate stage of a dog's development, without the proper guidance of a guru or religious leader like myself, the innocent pup may turn for his satisfactions towards deviant behaviour, and form an attachment to other males (the 'gay dog'), or to other species altogether (the 'dog in a manger'). For these and other groups, such as the self-abusers and dogs who dress up in little woolly coats, I offer a confidential advisory service. For a modest fee I can provide sound, practical, sympathetic guidance, and all cases are treated with the *utmost* discretion, replies in plain brown envelopes. Some of them make you crease up, like this one I got last week from a Cairn Terrier in Ffestiniog.

Dear Mr Barker,
Please, please can you help me as I don't know which way to turn. I am a Cairn Terrier, aged two and a half, and come from a line of healthy, normal boyos. We live in a grazing area of the National Park, look you, close to a field full of the most beautiful white fluffy bitches with sexy little high-heeled shoes. For many weeks I ran up and down the fence, ogling the talent inside, as they are quite the most excellent females anywhere in Wales, all round and cuddly, rather like poodles only with more meat on them. Last month I couldn't stand it any longer. I dug under the gate and got in, and after a terrible chase along the railway, with people hanging out of the carriages and calling the farmer, I managed to seize my prize and was about to have my wicked way with her when I received fourteen pellets in my backside. The farmer accused me of something terrible, but *I* didn't think she was all that worried. It's me that's worried, to tell the truth, and I can't sleep at night at all, as she said

not to touch her, *as she had been dipped.* Is it possible I have caught something? Will I be able to father pups in the future? I am out of my mind and desperate, and enclose a stamped addressed envelope.

Yours hopefully,
Fearful of Ffestiniog

Dear Fearful,
I pissed myself laughing at your letter. No, it is not possible for you to have puppies like this. You are barking up the completely wrong tree, as the animal you've got there is a sheep. Yes, they *do* carry diseases, some of them fatal, like foot and mouth, and there is also a danger of ticks. But the main worry is being shot at. I hope this goes some way to reassure you. Thank you for your remittance.

Yours sincerely,
Randy Barker

All these problems have arisen through dogs having been deflected from their normal, natural, healthy urges.

PEKINGESE: *'By Margaret Thatcher.'*

It has nothing to *do* with Margaret Thatcher!

PEKINGESE: *'Yes it does!'*

Have you written to Margaret Thatcher, explaining your problem?

PEKINGESE: *'Yes.'*

What did she say?

PEKINGESE: *'She said, "No funds are available at this time for help with small businesses of the type you describe." '*

And what type did you describe?

PEKINGESE: *'Canine leather and rubber gear.'*

Try the Manpower Services Commission's Enterprise Allowance scheme. Are there any other questions, before I return to my text? Any more interruptions, queries, asides, heckles or interjections you want to get off your chests? No? I can return to my subject, can I? Thank you so much, and if there are any more outbursts, I shall have the offenders ejected. This is all being taken down, you know, for my book.

Understanding your urges is an essential part of being a dog. Failure to understand your urges can lead to the sort of upsetting cases we have already described, of dogs being shot at and riding motorbikes, and so forth. Now, some urges are obviously more urgent than others. The urge to nibble a flea, or kick at the back of your ear, are very powerful drives which no dog can ignore, though some have actually done experiments to see how long they can resist an itch before bringing the claws into play, and the research may surprise you. A number of doctoral theses have been written on this subject in the past few years, not all of them by dogs, and the results show a depressing swing towards Pavlovian theory, but the current world record is held by a Coon Hound from Alabama and stands at 14.56 seconds – under dispute, as the dog in question has been accused of blood-doping and taking tranquillisers.

Another group of irresistible urges relate to the lavatorial functions. How long a dog can actually survive without passing water depends on several factors: the size and age of the dog, the amount he has drunk, the temperature of the environment, whether or not he can hear running water, bagpipes, and so on. The desire to relieve one's bowels, to eat, sleep, chase small worthless animals, murder, form canine collectives and political organs, supplant man and conquer the world – all these are powerful urges, and, when they occur, need attention at once. They impel a dog to act, and render him unconscious if he does not do so. But none of these urges is as strong or vital to our collective survival as the *urge to mate*. To intellectuals like myself, Jack Russell, Fang Gawd, Rin-Tin-Tin, G. H. Gnash and Cocker Leakie, who are the thinkers of our age, this sexual urge is the means by which the oppressed millions of dogdom will eventually throw off their collars and leads and chains and shackles and come to power, increasing their numbers beyond those of human kind so that we shall never again be put upon. *Alleluya, take me to the promised land.* To *you* (poor simple little sods) the urge is purely a matter of bodily desire and gratification, but never mind: our *ends* are the same!

How does an untrained dog distinguish between this vital sexual urge and, say, itching, or toilet needs, or mucking about in general? How does the adolescent dog tell the difference when he is torn this way and that by inner desires and disturbances? Well, it is possible to carry out certain tests. At the first sign of a powerful urge, here is what you should do. First, examine yourself to see if you can find a flea. If there is none, look carefully at your rear end. Does it appear normal? Are you suffering from irregularity or flatulence? If not, carry out a thorough inspection of your other organs. Do you have the correct number? Is body odour a problem? Are you worried about superfluous hair? Do you feel hot and faint? Are you

A male dog at a window can be very alluring

suffering from dizzy spells? If none of these appears to be the cause, and if nothing untoward is revealed in exhaustive physical examinations or the Eysenck Dog Personality Factor Test, then the chances are, you are experiencing a sexual urge – and here it is necessary to explain for the benefit of any puppies who may be listening, and with the utmost decorum and propriety, about the Birds and the Bees.

Birds are small feathery creatures that you might see sitting on a washing line. They are quite unlike bees, which are brown and furry, suck flowers and hum because they don't know the words. Both of these species are obeying Nature, and obedience to Nature should be your constant aim and inspiration, even if you are slightly confused about it. Be on the alert. Look out for passing members of our race in case they are female. Many pups have great difficulty discriminating between males and females, which in the case of human beings is often impossible and certainly illegal. But we dogs, if we are in the know, can tell the difference between a male and bitch (which is not a rude word, by the way, in our nomenclature). Here is what you do. Approach the animal in question in a confident, carefree manner, stating your name and breed (whether normal or Pedigree), and being careful to stand at an angle of about ninety degrees to the aforementioned questionable animal. Very subtly, during the course of conversation, hint that you may possibly have seen a juicy marrowbone lying in the road just behind him or her, and as he, she or it turns to investigate, quickly duck your head and glance at the underparts. If you see any appendages, forget it. If, however, you see nothing at all, then either the animal before you is a very *unlucky* dog, or you are a very *lucky* dog. The chances are, this is that exquisite thing, a female of our species: the she-dog, the lady-dog, the bitch, the fancy piece, the fluff, the business, the object of our desires. Some of you may never have seen one, having spent your entire lives locked up in human bondage, chained and drugged and kept indoors listening to heavy metal and punk-rock music. Don't despair! Keep fit and active! Practise the garden rush, and the gyratory leap that will spring you to freedom! One day, your day will come. In the meantime, keep your pheromones flowing: anoint your home, indoors and out, as this essence will carry your message for many a mile and attract passing females to your door. Draw attention to yourself. Pee on the piano. Preen yourself. Climb up on something so you can see out of the window – a male dog at a window can be very alluring to passing bitches, particularly if he has in his mouth some interesting object, like a ball or a rubber toy. Use your imagination, but whatever you do, remember the clarion call: obey Nature, and obey Randy Barker, and you won't go far wrong.

Chapter Three

Why Bitches are Bitches

Females are funny things. According to some male authorities, they do not actually qualify as proper dogs. A number of experts point to the waywardness and irrationality of bitches as a sign of mental illness, and research carried out by M. C. Pug, entitled 'A Metakinetic Study of Females in Greater Manchester', suggests that those in his sample had not yet reached the mental age of one. But whether or not you share M.C. Pug's conclusion that females are 'damn peculiar', what is beyond dispute is that they are very different from dogs (i.e. males, or proper dogs). And what is the nature of that difference? What is it that gives us the key to their uniqueness and distinctiveness, their separateness and non-maleness, and, in a word, their femininity?

GINGER MONGREL: *'Their bottoms?'*

Not their *bottoms*, no.

GREYHOUND: *'They have longer toenails.'*

Not *necessarily*. Think about this – what is it that females have, that male dogs do not? Yes, the Dachshund over there. You, yes. I thought you were about to say something.

DACHSHUND: *'I vass vundering if I could go outside.'*

Certainly not. If there is one principle –

DACHSHUND: *'I heff to.'*

POODLE: *'He's made a smell.'*

If there is one principle on which the bitch's unique sexual identity depends, that principle is the 'heat' or 'season'. The domestic bitch has two a year, unlike her wild cousin the she-wolf, who has just one, in February or March, by appointment only. Now, as young dogs, we have all, while our owners were out of the house, furtively pawed through the dictionary to look up 'heat', and what do we find there? 'Hotness; sensation of this; hot weather or climate; a single course in a race. *Heater*. Apparatus for heating a room or building.' None of which helps helps the young dog very much in his researches, and he becomes even more puzzled when he discovers that 'heat stroke' is 'prostration due to heat', which is associated in his mind with the prostate gland, and which sets him off writing to confidential advisory services. Yes!

DACHSHUND: *'I heff to go out!'*

Be quiet. So what the young dog needs at this stage is a definition of 'heat' which is more specific, and so next he looks up –

DACHSHUND: *'I heff to! Ich muss eine Wurst machen!'*

What does he say?

DOBERMANN: *'He says he's in the sausage business.'*

Let him out, for the love of Lassie. Now where was I? You lose your bloody thread. Yes, the young dog next looks up the definition of 'heat unit', and what does he find there? 'The amount of heat required to raise a pound of water one degree Fahrenheit in temperature (British thermal unit), or one gramme one degree Centigrade (calorie) or a kilogram (Kilocal).' Completely bemused by this, the growing pup sets to gnawing the dictionary and pulling individual pages out with his teeth, which he finds may then be chewed into papier-mâché pellets and pushed under the rug. But the bitch's heat, or to use the correct term, *oestrus*, remains a perpetual mystery, to drive him witless for the rest of his life.

What, then, is the oestrus? Well, literally translated, it means 'frenzy'. Most domestic bitches, therefore, have two 'frenzies' a year, and these last from eighteen to twenty-one days, though the female will only allow a dog to mate with her at the height of her frenzy. During the first ten days or so, she becomes particularly alluring, and she will announce her coming out, or 'pre-frenzy', by passing messages in pee code or the personal columns of the *Telegraph Pole*, to the effect that 'Miss X begs to inform male dogs in her locality that she is shortly to undertake a season, and is currently appearing in pre-frenzy showings at such-and-such. Invitations from suitable applicants welcome from 4 January,' and so forth. Prior to her getting out to pass these messages during her pre-frenzy, she scratches at the inside of her front door, or makes sickening squeaking noises on the windows with her claws, to draw

Scenting a bitch in season

attention to her predicament, and this is known as the 'pre-frenzy frenzy', or 'tizzwozz'. Humans seek to interfere with her at this stage, spraying her personal parts with deodorants containing harmful aerosols which upset Prince Charles and destroy the ozone layer, such as 'Dog off', 'Eau de Naff' and 'Oil of Citronella Extract Number Five', though these are fortunately quite ineffective. The world record for scenting a bitch in season is currently held by a Yorkshire Terrier from Ealing (I think this must be a misprint), and stands at 2.579 miles downwind. The bitch, between the tenth and fourteenth days of her *frenzy*, the *pre*-frenzy having culminated in a state of nymphomanic excitement, reaches what we call 'peak acceptance.'

PEKINGESE: *'Son of a gun!'*

During which she will stand to be served by what she considers a decent suitor, holding her tail aside. Of course, if she is a Pedigree, she will usually be tied up and gagged by human breeders prior to this ceremony taking place, in case she should set about a valuable stud and harm his career prospects. Finally, from the fourteenth day onwards, the bitch's interest is starting to flag and she will intersperse any sensual exchanges with remarks about pet mince and Dutch elm disease. By day 21 the whole frenzy is usually over. Any questions?

(Shocked silence.)

If the bitch has been mated during her frenzy, she will bear her offspring after a nine-week gestation period – gestation meaning, roughly, 'cooking and preparation time'. If she has *not* been mated, she may well suffer what is known in the veterinary profession as a pseudo or false pregnancy, triggered by the hormone progesterone in her body. This is when she starts vomiting in the fireplace and going off her food for no apparent reason, and she may also begin cuddling up to soft toys, or a cushion, or even a lump of wood. Many bitches who are falsely pregnant will actually produce milk for the phantom pups, become extremely tetchy and sensitive about their personal appearance, and refuse to leave the house in case they drop their bundles. We have all, I'm sure, experienced or overheard such scenes as this:

REX ROTTER:	Fancy meeting me outside the takeaway to sniff in the empty boxes, babe?
DAISY DUMPLING:	I can't. I've got a bun in the oven.
REX ROTTER:	You couldn't have. You've not been out for three weeks.
DAISY DUMPLING:	I have so.
REX ROTTER:	Nobody's been near you! What sort of bun is it – a hamburger?
DAISY DUMPLING:	Don't be ignorant. An angel came unto me and said, 'Fear not, for behold, I bring you glad tidings of a bun in the oven.' And lo, this bun came unto me.

REX ROTTER:	Show us. That's not a bun. That's a squeaky toy, you stupid bitch.
DAISY DUMPLING:	No, it's not – it's a bun, a little bun! I've made a nest for it in the coal bunker with rags and paper and I've dug up worms to feed it when it comes forth.
REX ROTTER:	It's a squeaky toy!
DAISY DUMPLING:	No, it's not.
REX ROTTER:	It is – look!
DAISY DUMPLING:	Don't you touch it, you wicked monster!
REX ROTTER:	It bloody squeaks, you see? (*Squeak Squeak Squeak.*) Besides, bitches don't have buns.
DAISY DUMPLING:	They don't?
REX ROTTER:	They have pups. Pups are small, smelly, mucky, wiggly little lumps of flesh with sticky-out eyes, that suckle bitches' chests, and sometimes there are fourteen of them and they tread and mess on you and gnaw you with their little needle-sharp teeth.
DAISY DUMPLING:	Which takeaway – the one in the High Street?

Our two-legged friends tend to spoil and overprotect bitches when they have these phantom pregnancies, and make a great song and dance over the 'poor girl' at this difficult time. Our next-door neighbours used to wheel theirs down the vet's in a pram. No, I'm serious. I looked up from the gatepost, and there was this bitch bouncing along the pavement in a bassinet! And there was nothing the matter with her! Of course, and this brings me to a general point, bitches do tend to suck up to humans much more than we do – they're more submissive than your average self-respecting male, licking faces and rolling on their backs to show their little pink bellies. What they'll do when the Revolution comes, I shudder to think. I expect they'll all be hand-rearing rubber ducks and vomiting in the back garden. The bitch has always been the Uncle Tom, or rather, the Auntie Two-legs, of dogdom. For generations, she has kowtowed to humans the whole time and shown us up. Still, some of them aren't bad, are they? Some of the 'sisters.' For the sake of our species, we males are prepared to forgive and forget, and put up with the peculiar little habits, the embarrassing fawning to our human oppressors, and the bitchy behaviour and bitchy biting that we've endured for centuries – though we can all point, can't we, brothers, to the scars! We all know of many a male, and many a private, injured in mating attempts with savage female customers!

DOG BRIGANDS, (*as one*): *'Damn right! Alleluya, brother!'*

And mortified feelings!

DOG BRIGANDS: *'Yes sir!'*

But we bear no ill will.

DOG BRIGANDS: *'Well, a little bit!'*

We are not misogynists; that is to say, we are not bitch-haters.

YORKSHIRE TERRIERS *(in unison):* *'Speak for thee roody self!'*

Some of you smaller ones may indeed have lost limbs, or been fatally wounded, trying to seduce larger breeds. You have my sympathy, especially the fatalities among you. Are there any here tonight?

GEOFFREY THE YORKIE: *'Aye, there's woon dead over 'ere. 'Ee were all reet 'till roody Dalmatian bitch got 'old of 'im.'*

I'm so sorry. Whereabouts was it that she attacked him?

GEOFFREY THE YORKIE: *'Outside 'Eadingley cricket ground. 'Ee knew 'ee weren't allowed in, but 'ee got through fence quite frequent, as 'ee liked t' see play. 'Ee once roon ont' pitch to see 'is 'ero Boycott make 'oondred against the Australians. 'Ee were named after t' cricketer, were little Geoff.'*

But I thought *your* name was Geoff.

GEOFFREY THE YORKIE: *'Oh aye – we're all named Geoff after t' cricketer. Foony, entit.'*

Yes – a sad loss there to our Yorkshire brothers. A lad cut down in his prime by a heartless female. 'Who can count the cost when little ones are lost, or fail to catch a whiff, when little ones are stiff?' Perhaps you could lay our little brother to rest now, Yorkshire brethren. Thank you. *Alleluya. Amen.* Let the cortège pass through into the backyard please.

(Dog Brigands howl softly as the funeral procession makes its way through the throng, to the strains of 'Oh shepherd dog, thy bones on high', Dog Hymnal, No. 404.)

Let us not be bitter, brothers. Not all female dogs stand accused of so callous a crime. Let us not forget that they are our sisters of the Revolution, and that some of them have endured harsh fangs themselves! And in defence of our sisters (and our aunties, mothers-in-law and assorted mates): female dogs are, much more frequently than we are, the victims of that most repressive of Two-legged measures, *neutering*. They are routinely spayed. Let each of you consider this for a moment. 'Spayed' is not a likeable word, and it is not a likeable thing. But do we *really* understand, as males, what it must mean?

BLACK LABRADOR: *'I do – I think it's a sign of a police state. I think it's an outrageous, terrible crime against the public.'*

You mean against the female dogs, surely.

BLACK LABRADOR: *'Against anyone who happens to be in the street at the time. They can't all be rioters, can they!'*

Do what?

BLACK LABRADOR: *'Well, I like water – that's my breeding. But a lot of people don't. The police give them a couple of warnings, and then if they don't disperse, that's it, they are spayed. It's not good enough. Water cannons cost lives.'*

I think you may have hold of the wrong end of the stick there, actually. *Spayed!* What do I mean by *spayed?* What's the matter with you lot! I don't know why I bother. Yes.

ST BERNARD: *'Is it a gardening implement?'*

No.

GERMAN SHEPHERD: *'A fairly dark-skinned human being?'*

No – SPAYED. S.P.A.Y.E.D. Anybody? To do with sex . . . Yes?

GINGER MONGREL: *'Is it when they have their legs apart?'*

No, that's *splayed.* Tst! Oh, what is it *NOW?*

DOBERMANN: *'May little Hansie come back in? He's been scratching for quite a while.'*

Let him in. (*Sigh.*) Let them all in. Let everybody in.

(*Hansie the Dachshund enters and returns to his place.*)

I don't suppose you know what *spayed* means either, do you. Any ideas? *Spayink?*

HANSIE THE DACHSHUND: *'Surgical removal of ze voom and ovaries.'*

That's *right. Surgical removal of the womb and ovaries.* Spaying is widely recommended by vets for non-breeding female dogs as a means of birth control!

(*Gasps of shock, horror and outrage.*)

True, and it is, of course, a major mutilation, much worse than all the other snippings and removals inflicted on Pedigree tails, ears and dewclaws. And *this* quite unnecessary and outrageous operation is carried out on bitches of all ages who would otherwise be bearing future soldiers for the Revolution. Not content with spraying bitches' hindquarters with deodorants; not content with bombarding their bodies with contraceptive pills and injections, they have to remove a vitally important and very active system, namely the reproductive organs – the loss of which may affect the female dogs concerned for the rest of their lives.

The following interview was recorded in a secret location in an extremely dark coal cellar, with a bitch we shall refer to simply as 'Mavis'. Members of her family, her solicitor and social worker were also present at the interview, though some of them had to go outside after being trodden on.

DUKE DOUGAL:	Mavis, you recently underwent the surgical procedure known as 'spaying' at your local veterinary clinic.
'MAVIS':	I'm not Mavis. I'm Hattie Hobnail of Chesterfield.
DUKE DOUGAL:	No, 'Mavis' is your pretend name – you remember we explained, about protecting your identity – remember?
'MAVIS':	Oh, yes. Yes.
DUKE DOUGAL:	What happened, Mavis, when you were taken to the clinic?
'MAVIS':	They stuck me with a sharp spine and put me to sleep, and when I woke up, they'd done me.
DUKE DOUGAL:	You found that you had had an ovario-hysterectomy.
'MAVIS':	Oh yes, and I'd been completely spayed, Desmond.
DUKE DOUGAL:	How long ago was it?
'MAVIS':	Last year, and as you can see, I'm ruined by it. I couldn't jump up or do anything until the stitches were taken out, and then I started putting on all this weight. I can't get into my bean bed any more *(sniff)*, and I'm now grossly overweight at four and a half stone, Desmond. And then my mate left me for the young bull terrier bitch from the laundry.
DUKE DOUGAL:	Your mate left you on account of your weight problem?
'MAVIS':	Yes, Desmond – he told her I was a cripple and could no longer satisfy his needs.
DUKE DOUGAL:	I'm not Desmond.
'MAVIS':	Sorry?
DUKE DOUGAL:	You keep calling me Desmond.
'MAVIS':	Aren't you Desmond Wilcox, the BBC interviewer?
DUKE DOUGAL:	No, I'm Duke Dougal of K9P Airwaves.

'MAVIS':	Oh, dear me.
DUKE DOUGAL:	Were you warned of the possible side effects?
'MAVIS':	I thought they said Desmond Wilcox.
DUKE DOUGAL:	Did they warn you of the dangers before the operation?
'MAVIS':	No, they never.
DUKE DOUGAL:	And you have now found that you can no longer have puppies?
'MAVIS':	(Sob)
DUKE DOUGAL:	This must have been a terrific blow.
'MAVIS':	Yes. I've only had the twelve and – (sob).
DUKE DOUGAL:	I understand.
'MAVIS':	It's all over. And the worst thing was that now I've found out, I've got this other problem as well.
DUKE DOUGAL:	And can you tell us about that?
'MAVIS':	I've–I've–(she breaks down).
DUKE DOUGAL:	Take your time, Mavis. What is the other problem?
'MAVIS':	I've started smoking heavily. (She breaks down again.)
DUKE DOUGAL:	Your owner knew about the operation before it happened?
'MAVIS':	Oh yes – he took me down there and paid for it (sniff).
DUKE DOUGAL:	And does he feel any responsibility for your predicament? (Mavis shakes her head.) What does he say about the effect on your life?
'MAVIS':	He says to keep my paws off his pipe.

I hope that every dog in this room, and every dog reading this book, will take to heart the sad case of Mavis. I hope that each and every one of you, when the time comes, will be prepared to lay down his life to prevent such attacks on our women-folk, and bite for what is right in the coming Uprising, to ensure that *never again* is any healthy dog subjected to surgical interference of this kind. Let us proclaim our physical integrity! Let us bark it from the rooftops! *What do we want?*

DOG BRIGANDS: *'Freedom from cuts!'*

When do we want it?

DOG BRIGANDS: *'Now!'*

Chapter Four

Step One to Success: Getting Out

Every dog is a potential mater. What is a mater? A mater is a dog who is able, by his six wits, to go forth and propagate his kind according to Nature's laws. Not all maters are male dogs: there have been one or two very famous she-dogs who have 'gone forth' – one thinks immediately of Mater Hari and Alma Mater. But most maters of note have been male, by reason of the fact that we are usually the ones clever enough to get out on the streets.

Of course, I do not need to tell the dog brigands and freebooters here tonight about the importance of getting on the streets. Each one of you knows, Pedigrees included, that if we stay indoors, contemplating our goolies, the only two possibilities are that we shall either be mated with a clone crated across the country and forced on us by humans, or – as is the case with Mongrels like myself – not mated at all! I have sired 1,342 pups, and mean to go on spreading the Randy Barker genes from coast to coast!

(Gasps of wonder and admiration.)

And I didn't do *that* by staying indoors. *Out and about* – these should be your watchwords. And we Mongrels have brought street-raking virtually to an art form. By far the great majority of dogs in our canine prisons and shelters are Mongrels, picked up while going about our legitimate natural business and charged with loitering offences which usually carry the death penalty unless a Two-legs can be found to bail us out. Let me tell you what those Mongrels on death row dream about. In a far country called France, there is a place called the Garden of Versailles. I've never seen it myself, though many dogs who have had what we call 'Near Death Experiences' have seen visions of this particular Garden. It stretches as far as the eye can see, and dogs roam in it freely, even now, drinking out of fountains and sunning their bellies without let or hindrance, except that a lot of humans clutter the place up with cars and pushchairs at the moment – we shall have to do something about that. Every dog's dream is to wander about freely in the Garden of Versailles, and after the Great Uprising, dogs will storm the place and take up residence, having our meat delivered in vans. Humans will be allowed in but only on leads and under proper control, and they will be taken for walks when it is quite convenient, and not before. And if they play us up in *any* way, shape or form, they won't go. They will get a good hiding. But if they are very good, they will be permitted to live in harmony with us in the Promised Land. *Alleluya.*

DOG BRIGANDS: *'Take me, oh take me to the Promised Land*
Where all my bones will be laid down;
Where firm dogs walk without a frown,
Free from the smack of human hand.'

But until that day, brothers, until that day, we must be vigilant. We must be street-wise. We must seize every opportunity to escape from our confinement to ensure some female dog's confinement.

GINGER MONGREL: *'Clever play on words, there, brother Barker. Wo!'*

Now, although I myself have sired 1,342 pups during my escapes, I am not actually a stud dog. I am only an amateur.

(Cries of: 'Never! Randy for Dogfather! Randy for King!')

No, really. I'm not even in *Famous Stud Dogs of Our Time*. You know why? Because all the dogs in there are sodding Pedigrees – sorry – they are Pedigrees in there, and great names among them, who should be a source of inspiration to us all. Names like: Champion Star Stud Bang Boy, who fathered 3,691 pups and dropped dead on the job. Champion Bigbum Beloved of Mountfrequent – he sired 4,409, some of whom went on to become renowned Mountfrequent champions themselves. Then there was the noted Champion Hotboots Lovely Grub of the Endaway Kennels in Herts, and his stablemates Champion Napoleon Backside and Champion Graceful Legover. Between them they sent litters all over the world. And who can forget Champion 'Kinky' Knockalot of Fartingforth, sire of 6,300 in the Midlothian district? Or English and American Champion Ballbearing Classic of Tinseltown? I do not bother to call to mind their 'breeds', as we are trying to get above that sort of thing in matters of genetic engineering. Besides, terms like 'Toy' and 'Standard' and 'Shorthaired' tend to rather tarnish the names on our roll of honour – names such as Champion Deaf to Dismay Bluebeard Poopoo; Champion Weary Willie of Butchhaven Tenderloin, and Champion Upandover Dirty Lad of Tiddlesfield. Yes, I can see some of you Pedigrees in the audience are already moved to tears. And how about this one – Champion *Bouncy Bouncy Binky Bonk*, sire of the famous Bonker dynasty? Makes your eyes water, doesn't it? In fact, it's difficult for a Mongrel like myself to express his precise feelings about stud dogs like *Bouncy Bouncy Binky Bonk*. (At least in public.) But the *real* champion studs are not these pampered Pedigrees at all.

POODLE: *'Yes they are!'*

Be quiet. The *real* champions, my friends, are the dogs out there on the streets! The freelancers. The Pedigrees who have succeeded in getting over the kennel wall and making a living for themselves in the natural world. And the Mongrels, who have, since time immemorial, been working away at keeping our race alive and in tune with the requirements of Nature. *Real* studs, like Mad Mo Carlot of Manhattan, and Wily Oats of Wichita. And Clarence N'Dongo of Harare – ever heard of him? You won't find *his* name listed in *Dogbretts*, but he's sired more pups than your Bouncy Bouncy Binky Bonks have had hot dinners. Oh yes. These are the names to tell your grandchildren. These are the true champions. Dogs like Threeball Casey of Fort Wayne, Indiana, and his sons 'Wild' Jed, Cowpoke and Stickup; little Monsieur Pepe la Rage of Paris; Hoffie Hundinhopper of Hamburg; 'Dipper' Dingo Kelly of Wagga Wagga. And British studs to be proud of, too, like 'Sly' Sid the Sod of Stepney; and 'Awful' Alfie Ackright of 'Uddersfield; and 'Harmful' Horace Headbanger of Hartlepool. Not forgetting Scots star of the north, 'Wee' Sandy McRake of Glasgow, whose exploits are celebrated in whines and howls from Battersea to Bombay. These are the real ones! These are the living legends, the heroes of our age! And how did they come to glory? By getting out on the streets and sidewalks. *Out and about. Am I right?*

DOG BRIGANDS: *'Out and about! Out and about!'*

A word of advice about making your escape plans. Always think ahead. Many a dog has made a complete wally of himself by jumping over an enormous fence and then having to come back in again through the gate because he's forgotten something. Be prepared.

What you will need

Before you escape, spend some time and thought on your Necessaries. These are some of the essential Necessaries for any dog planning a permanent escape bid (i.e. not coming back through the gate).

2½ lb of pet mince	assorted crêpe bandages
one marrow or shank bone	small bottle of antiseptic

Some of the essential Necessaries

3 lb of tripe (best)
a dozen chewsticks
¼ lb boiled sweets
one bar milk chocolate
several sausages
one towel
a squeaky toy (for trading)
travel-sick pills
distemper vaccine (if available)

styptic pencil
tourniquet
splint
wig, Arab head-dress or other disguise
bedding
maps of the district
A to Z for London area
water dish

You often find other materials you need along the way, and it is possible to improvise with items found in nature and in dustbins. Bedding may be tied round the body for extra mobility; other Necessaries should be folded into a neat bundle and packed in a plastic bag.

Breaking out

If you are breaking out for the first time, plan your move carefully. Memorise the methods described in this chapter, as you will otherwise have to keep ducking to the bookshelves to consult my book, and this may arouse suspicion. If you are breaking *in* – as, for example, to a bitch's premises, or your own after all hope has foundered – remember to follow the instructions in the reverse order. Always choose the easiest method of escape. *Don't* try to make a name for yourself hang-gliding or riding a motorbike (unless you are very experienced). Be on the alert for the unexpected opening. If your human takes you out in a car, for example, you may be presented with labour-saving gaps in windows and doors. Many dogs are exercised off the lead with a ball or stick. If you are one of these lucky ones, you can escape as easy as pie. To avoid giving cause for alarm, return one or two throws normally before making off in completely the opposite direction. This will give you the advantage of surprise.

For the more homebound dog, there are two 'easy pickings'. One is to wait until visitors arrive, and push past them through the front door amid the confusion. This method is especially effective if the visitor is lame or has large numbers of children to be brought into the house. But remember – you will still have to negotiate the fence or gate. The other short cut to freedom is for homebound dogs whose owners are keen gardeners. Wait until the owner is bending near the fence working on his herbaceous border, and leapfrog over his back,

Wait until the owner is bending near the fence

using it as a springboard to launch you into the street. (It may also be possible to hide in the compost heap until some suitable gate-opening opportunity presents itself.)

The *dis*advantage of all these 'short cut' methods, of course, is that it will be difficult for you to have your Necessaries about you at the time of the escape. You might consider tying your bedding round you some weeks previously, so that your owner becomes accustomed to seeing you wearing it about the house. And it may be possible to conceal a few of the other essential items within the folds without these becoming too apparent (for instance your sausages and tourniquet). Finally, before deciding on any of the following methods, do a recce of the perimeter of your premises, sniffing carefully behind bushes and hedges and keeping an eye out for small holes in the fence or wall which may be worked to your advantage. (If your home is surrounded by a moat, this may not be possible.) Avoid electric fences at all times, and if there are searchlights, work only during the day, pretending your ball has accidentally rolled near the boundary (this method was invented by a human called Steve McQueen in *The Great Escape*).

There are three ways of getting out of an enclosure, basically – *under, over* or *through.*

Under – the tunnelling method

Always dig in a corner of the garden farthest away from human eyesight. Notice which windows are most used by your humans for goggling out of, and select a spot on the other side of the building. Unless you are a breed accustomed to being seen digging, such as a Jack Russell or Basset Hound, have with you a conspicuous bone or dead rodent, so that you appear to be making a hole for some innocuous purpose. Avoid using heavy equipment such as compressors or pneumatic drills, as these may attract attention.

If you are dealing with a wooden fence of sticks or palings, examine them carefully to see which ones are rooted in the soil, and avoid digging at these, or the whole fence may collapse on top of you. You should also beware of digging under trees, as this is very time-consuming and you are liable to get tangled up in the roots. Be sensible. If you find yourself digging under a pond, or if you strike a gas main or electric cable, run immediately for help. Do not try to repair the damage yourself. Aim at a section of the wall or fence which rests on the topsoil, and dig furiously but without panic. Allow sufficient clearance for your body to squeeze through comfortably. A hole six feet in diameter is quite unnecessary and may arouse suspicion. Do not waste time attempting to shore up your tunnel with wooden props etc. Get through as quickly as possible.

If you are attempting to tunnel out under railings, think carefully. It may be possible to squeeze through instead, and this will save you valuable time and energy. But you must first measure and test the gap, to avoid getting stuck. This is done by using next door's cat. If the cat can be pushed through the railings fairly easily *without* forcing, the next stage is to ease one of your rear legs very carefully through, until your buttock is resting on the railings. If this test is successful, grease the body with lard by rubbing the shoulders against the Sunday joint and then, working slowly and carefully, ease the body between the railings, but remember – always begin at the rear. This way, in the event of your getting stuck, it will appear you are trying to gain access to your own premises and you will avoid punishment. Never, never stick your head between railings, as sometimes the fire brigade may be too preoccupied with trivialities like fires to saw you out.

Over

If you live in kennels with concrete runs, or your garden has a solid floor, such as asphalt or crazy paving, your best method is to attempt a fence- or wall-leap. However, for all leaps, you *must* spend time getting yourself fit beforehand, and I have been asked by my publishers to *stress* the dangers of unfit, elderly or fat dogs becoming impaled on fences and obstacles. *Don't take chances.* If you are unsure about your fitness, practise for a minimum of two weeks using an A-frame (which may be obtained from police dog-training schools), or get your Two-legs to hold a stick or other suitable object at arm's length, so that you can try out your leaping techniques, gradually gaining height. Recce your premises carefully. Look for the lowest spot in your enclosure. Even a medium sized Mongrel can clear six feet with the proper training, as Bambi Mitchell of Newport just off the M11 has shown. (Her record to date is 7 feet 3.28 inches over a wire-netting gate at Wood Green Animal Shelter.) Indeed, a Yorkshire Terrier in America is able to escape from his premises by pulling up the wire-netting fence with his teeth and claws, and has been seen doing it on television.

There are several methods of leaping, but in each case the important thing to remember is to avoid breaking the legs on impact when you land on the other side, as this may hamper your escape.

a) the standing-start jump

Suitable for walls and fences sloping slightly away, so that it is possible to scuttle up the side. Probably requires more strength than other methods, but has the advantage of being useful in a confined working space where no run-up is available. Compress the body to the ground and, pushing off as hard as you can with your rear legs and hips, stretch the body forward, hooking the forepaws over the wall and using your forelegs to heave you across, scuttling the back legs as you go, to gain momentum.

b) the running jump

The essence of this jump lies in getting up a good head of steam before leaving the ground, and the further you run, the more momentum you should build up for the coming obstacle. If it is possible to begin your run-up from upstairs in the house, with all the doors open, this is ideal, but avoid fagging yourself out and falling down exhausted in front of the wall.

c) the gyratory leap

This method is the one I use, having perfected it in secret trials while my owner wasn't looking. It does require a level of athleticism few non-Mongrels can attain without special training (my coaching courses are held annually at the Waterworks, Epping Forest, fees payable in advance in case of injury). The beauty of this method is that it enables you to land on all fours, spreading the stress on impact to avoid leg and shoulder damage. Begin with the run-up as in Method (b), but on your approach to the obstacle, *turn slightly sideways*, tucking the feet in tightly on take-off to avoid catching them on the fence during flight. Allow at least six inches clearance to safeguard landing gear. Your leap should carry you over the wall *sideways on*, and has the advantage of enabling you to keep one eye on the house as you go over. Breeds with notoriously weak shoulder structures, such as GSDs, should adopt this method wherever possible. Keep your weight distribution even at all times, as there is the possibility of tilting at the apex, in which case you are a certainty for the veterinary surgery.

d) the platform method

For small dogs unable to use their teeth and claws on wire-netting as described above, it will be necessary to build a platform or launch pad at the jump-off point. This may best be done in a quiet corner of the fence, using bricks, refuse or droppings piled up over a period of time and reinforced with stones or pieces of wood. If necessary, displace a pile of soil or compost from elsewhere but do not use a wheelbarrow as this will alert the owner to your activities.

Whichever leaping technique you use, always check beforehand what lies over the wall or fence and avoid, if possible, landing on top of passing pedestrians or in heavy traffic.

Through

If you can neither leap nor burrow your way to freedom, don't despair. It may be feasible for you to exit via a door or window, if either gives onto the street. In any case, all escapees should be aware of doors and windows, as they may impede progress in getting from the building into the garden in the first place.

a) doors

The two most important doors are the 'front' door and the 'back' door. Other doors within the house tend to lead into other rooms, which may not be of benefit. There are two types of doors: those which open inwards, and those which open outwards. Usually, 'front' and 'back' doors open inwards, but this may be ascertained by the same testing method as for 'railings', by using next door's cat, or by doing simple experiments with your nose and paws. Doors left ajar are an obvious bonus, but doors which are simply pushed to, without the catch or lock being properly secured, provide ample escape opportunities. If they are outward-opening, simply nudge gently with the nose. If they are inward-opening, like the 'front' or 'back' doors, push very gently with your nose to nudge the door out of its socket with a slight bounce. When you have a little gap, hook the claws round the edge and pull the door gently. If you have hold of the right side, it should ease towards you without any bother, so that you can then hook your head round and swing it open. Do not waste your time trying to pull open doors which are away-opening. These types of doors can only be operated by the pushing method.

b) windows

Windows, like doors, come in two types. They may be either *up*stairs or *down*stairs windows. If they are of the first type, take extra care when jumping out, as dogs have been seriously injured landing from great heights in the middle of motorways or busy road junctions. *Check before jumping*. If you are wearing your bedding, it may be possible to land safely from the second floor, but don't be overambitious. Downstairs windows are always best.

Whichever you choose, remember that both window types come in two subcategories: they may be downstairs and open, downstairs and closed, upstairs and open or upstairs and closed. The last method is pretty rough and should not be attempted on a full stomach. If you are wearing your bedding, ensure that it is well tucked in. If you are *not* wearing your bedding, you are a bloody nutcase and should definitely be certified. All dogs attempting the closed-window method should seek professional advice beforehand by writing to me and enclosing last wills, testaments and stamped addressed envelopes. (I am able to undertake executor work at weekends only.)

Special tips for window-jumpers:

a) If you are making a closed-window attempt, check carefully before you jump the type of glass you are dealing with. Tap with the forepaw and sniff the surface at *at least* three check points. *Never* attempt to jump through leaded fancy lattice work or double glazing. Better to stay home and wait for rescue.

b) If you are naming me in your will as a beneficiary, my full title is: Prof. Dr Sir Randy Stanley Beau Brummell Fitz-Mutt Barker PhD OBE, but you don't have to put all that on the envelope. It's just a legal trifle.

The chimney method

This is a different method altogether from the ones described above. If you have failed at everything else you might like to try this one. First, locate the hearth. Some houses have several hearths, especially if they are very old (over twelve years). If you find a hearth, examine it carefully. Has it been bricked up? Is the fire alight? If the answer to either of these questions is 'yes', do not attempt to escape straightaway. Await the summer and/or conversion work. Do not attempt your escape on Christmas Eve, in any case, as there may be a danger of collision mid-flue with a pair of large, red-velvet-covered buttocks. If you have carried out all the necessary checks and the flue is clear, jump carefully into the aperture above the hearth and squeeze or wiggle towards the ring of light at the top of the chimney. When you get out at the other end, play it by ear. Try to avoid rolling down the roof into next door's garden barking and screaming and clinging onto the slates in an ignominious manner.

NB: Larger breeds should not attempt this method wearing bedding, for fear of what we professionals call 'stickage'.

The manhole method

In the very famous human film *The Third Manhole* a character called 'Welles' very nearly escapes from Vienna by running through the sewage system. Inspired by this movie, many dogs have attempted to penetrate their local drainage by climbing down wells or pushing their heads down the toilet bowl. These sewage assaults are quite pointless. The U-bend in the toilet is *designed* to prevent dogs swimming down the pipes – even a Chihuahua may encounter difficulties. The only way into the sewers is via a suitable manhole, and if you are planning this sort of escape, you should look for a manhole cover in the garden. When you have located one, here is what you should do. Using a metal stick such as a poker or big screwdriver – a crowbar is ideal if you have one to paw – work away at the side of the cover and lever up the edge. Do not attempt to lift the lid with your teeth (as this will result in loss of teeth). When you have dislodged the cover sufficiently, attract the attention of a stupid-looking Two-legs (your owner will usually be fairly suitable) and begin barking frantically at the little gap you have made. The Two-legs will naturally think you have lost a very important item down the manhole, such as a puppy, a glass eye or the budgerigar, and will heave off the lid immediately. Once you are down the manhole, run like blazes, if possible without inhalation.

Warning: This method should not be attempted by dogs who cannot swim, unless they have access to a snorkel set in working order.

The dustbin method

If you are a completely useless escaper, and have tried all the other methods in this chapter and buggered them up, your only hope is the dustbin ploy. For this method, which is quite dangerous, you will need to carry out a thorough casing, recce or investigation beforehand of the refuse-collection routine of your household. Your life may depend on the accuracy of your research, so *do it right*. If your dustbin is emptied weekly, and *if* the bin is placed outside your garden for this purpose, here is the plan. After a collection has been made and the dustbin returned to its normal position, wait until nobody is looking. Then, wearing a plastic bag on your head and the minimum of bedding around your person (because space inside the dustbin may be at a premium), jump into the bin and slide the lid over your head. Remain inside the dustbin for a week. Do not whine or cry out when rubbish is emptied into the bin, as this will arouse suspicion. Sit quietly underneath the accumulating rubbish doing yoga or committing to memory the names of the famous stud dogs in this chapter. As soon as you feel the dustbin being lifted and carried out of the garden for refuse collection, concentrate carefully. Wait until the bin is set down, and then – *without* stopping to check your bedding, luggage or personal appearance – leap with all your might out of the bin and set off down the street. If you do this correctly and at the appropriate moment, you will have surprise on your side and will usually be in luck, with a clear run in any direction your choose. Your owner will generally not be expecting a dog wearing a plastic bag and a bedding loincloth to spring suddenly out of the rubbish. If, on the other hand, you delay until the *second* lift and hear a strange grinding noise, you are in no luck whatsoever.

What to do if caught

If there is a foul-up in any of the escape methods I have suggested, do not improvise. Have a plan ready. Choose one of the following:

1. Pretend to have amnesia. Sway about, turning your head from side to side, as though you have lost your sense of direction.
2. Pretend you were running an important errand, or looking for a burglar. Bark furiously, as though on the scent of a dangerous hoodlum, and keep looking anxiously up and down the street.
3. The moment you are discovered outside the property, turn immediately *inwards*, as though trying to gain access to it. Look baffled.
4. Lick the Two-legs profusely, whine and whinny, as though greeting a long-lost friend. This will make your human think he or she has lost you by some carelessness and that you are pleased and relieved to be home. (Be careful to hide any maps, luggage etc.)

5. Act contrite. Fawn on the ground, making your body as small, low and cowering as possible. Tuck your tail under, lower your ears and squeeze up your eyes as though in pain and fear. Make little pathetic whining noises.
6. If all else fails, feign dead and play for time.

Finally, brethren

If you *are* successful, and get out onto the street, don't panic from the shock. Try not to look suspicious. Trot boldly along the centre of the pavement or sidewalk, head and tail held high as though going about your routine business. Wag at passers-by, but without committing yourself. Do not tip over dustbins in broad daylight – you may be exposing a fellow escapee. Stow your bedding, luggage etc. in a secure hiding place. Avoid heavy traffic and vans with ladders on the top marked 'Dog Warden'. And finally, keep in touch with other dogs by the pee code (see Chapter 5), so that you are aware of local events and activities, female talent in your area, important political meetings and so on.

You are now a genuine freebooter. Good luck to you – and remember: bite for what is right!

Chapter Five

Step Two: Reading the Pee Code

Humans, for all their power and tyranny, are dim. How do I know for a fact that humans are dim? Because with all their new-fangled technology, not one of them has succeeded in cracking the urinary code, vulgarly known to you all as the Pee Code, or *Chumfo*. If they could break it, of course, we should be in dead trouble. Humans would be dropping eaves on top of us, and contaminating our messages with bugs and plants. As you know, ladybirds and stinging nettles, in particular, can interfere with our delicate chemical traces and completely alter the meaning. The simple message, 'Hansie the Dachshund called, and you were out, dear Putzie' can be corrupted by plant or beetle deposits to 'Hansie the Hound called out, "You deaf old pisspot" ' – which could easily wreck a budding relationship with the attractive young bitch of Hansie's acquaintance.

When you get out and about on the streets and leave your messages, most of you will not be thinking about the scientific side of what you are doing. The inter-dog language of love, or CHUMFO (Coded Hydrotropic Urinary Monitoring Frenzy Olfaction), is actually only a small branch of the dog's legendary scenting and chemical decoding capabilities which have baffled mankind for centuries. How is it, they wonder, that 'mere' dogs can hunt and track better than they can? How is it that we can predict deaths and homecomings, and tell the time without a wristwatch? How do we manage to find their drugs, their firearms, their bombs, their mines, their flight recorders, their avalanche victims, their fugitives and their belongings, to say nothing of conger eels, truffles and other goodies they've asked us to search for over the years? How do we do it with no trouble at all, wagging our tails to show it was a piece of cake, while they're all struggling with their anomaly detectors, drug-abuse urine calibrators, geiger counters and computers?

Most of them don't even know we've got chemical glands between our toes for scraping and marking Chumfo messages. Most of them have never heard of our Tailbase gland for

Contaminating our messages with bugs and plants

depositing coded traces on our waste products. They think the reason we go about sniffing other dogs' droppings is because we are 'dirty'. Why do they imagine we chop and chatter our teeth together, and taste the air, and rattle our jaws, if not to decipher important chemical messages? Pathetic, isn't it? Which one of you poor little underestimated sods has ever had a human take the trouble to look inside his mouth to see the two little apertures in the roof with which we decode scent and taste information? One bloke did have a look in a dog's mouth once. His name was Jacobson. 'Here, come and have a look at this,' he says. 'This dog's got two little holes in the roof of his mouth. Wonder what they're for?' And ever since, the apertures have been known as 'Jacobson's organs', as though they were *his* bloody organs. Yes. Human beings may talk a lot, but they haven't got a great deal 'upstairs'.

They can't get over what they call our 'sense of smell', can they? They think it's amazing what we can do. They were all over the moon about a dog in the First World War who tracked his owner from Hammersmith to Armentières and found him in a trench. And they have to take their hats off to an RAF police dog like Brandy Goldenballs, a yellow lab cross who has found 4040 kilos of drugs worth £4 million, including 97 pounds of herbal cannabis behind heavy steel doors on a ship, consignments hidden in bath salts, chilli powder, antiseptic and 'dog smells', and 400 grammes of herbal cannabis wrapped in four plastic bags, bound with Sellotape and suspended in a tank of coolant fluid.

There are 'drug-sniffers' like Brandy working for humans all over the world. To say nothing of all the pathfinders and so-called 'mine-sniffers' who can detect plastic as easily as metal, like the ones who work for the Army up at Melton Mowbray. They even had a veterinary surgeon remove the dogs' scent glands and they could still find the mines, no problem. Funny, isn't it? The Army in Northern Ireland had a dog indicate on a brick wall and found a rifle that had been cemented up for twenty-five years. What 'scent' is that, they wonder? Of course, they know how we find a gun in a scrap metal yard – scrap metal hasn't got gun oil or cordite on it, so that's a doddle for us. But how do we find truffles? A good truffle dog can detect 300–400 pounds of truffles in a week – and that's an awful lot of dog biscuits.

How do we find fugitives? Before breeders ruined them Bloodhounds once helped police get a conviction on a scent twenty hours old. American trackers found convicted killer James Earl Ray hiding in the hills of east Tennessee. Any decent police dog can pick out a man in a crowded factory and say, 'Cop 'old of this one.' Scientists are beginning to talk about dogs detecting 'thermal' differences and 'density' differences. They think it might have something to do with a little infra red heat receptor they haven't yet quite been able to discover.

(Tittering breaks out.)

Or that dogs can pick up 'disturbances' in the environment, such as vibrations before an earthquake – Hansie the Dachshund, what *are* you doing?

HANSIE THE DACHSHUND: *'Vot em I doink?'*

Reggie Ruffin's a *male* Border Collie. You knew that, did you? Then why are you mounting and treading on him like that?

HANSIE THE DACHSHUND: *'I heff to climb up, to see in ze mouse of ziss Bloodhound! To look at ze little organs.'*

It's not just Bloodhounds who heff ze little organs. We all heff ze little organs. Have a look in one of the Geoffreys' mouths.

HANSIE THE DACHSHUND: *'Nein. Cannot!'*

Why is that?

HANSIE THE DACHSHUND: *'Zey heff bad bress.'*

YORKIES: *'Watch theeseln, thee black puddin' pillock!'*

(Snarling and yapping racket.)

Stop that! Hansie the Dachshund, get down at once. Do me the courtesy! Thank you. Now, I shan't tell you again. Any more brainless interludes and that's your lot. Am I clear? All right. So, humans are completely baffled by our olfactory expertise. By the fact that, even if a dog is a relatively poor smeller, he can detect and analyse upwards of 2,500,000 units of scent information – yes?

GEOFFREY THE YORKIE: *'Aye, there's a relatively poor smeller over 'ere.'*

Shut up.

GEOFFREY THE YORKIE (2): *'And 'e's a reet German stinker an' all!'*

(Uproar.)

Right – that's it.

(Randy Barker signals to a team of spike-collared henchdogs. The Yorkies and Hansie the Dachshund are very roughly flung out in the backyard, screaming and yelling.)

(Shocked silence.)

To return to my text. Yes?

DOBERMANN: *'Excuse me, but may I know why little Hansie has been put out?'*

You want to join him?

DOBERMANN: *'No.'*

You want to take over? You want to give these lectures?

DOBERMANN: *'No, sir, but –'*

Good. Refill my waterbowl. Come on, come on! You – open the door for him. So, as I was saying, even a dog who is a relatively poor smeller can detect upwards of 2.5 million trace elements, subdivided, of course, into the eight scent categories, which are? *Which are?*

DOG BRIGANDS *(chanting, as of times tables):* *'Chumfo, snuzzles, spoors, air-omas, kemapoos, fragrins, odornomes and miasmas.'*

OK – what's a snuzzle? The Cocker Spaniel?

COCKER SPANIEL: *'Non-dog animal trace.'*

And what's a spoor?

COCKER SPANIEL: *'Non-dog animal trail.'*

Right. What's the difference between an air-oma and an odornome – the little fellow at the front, there. Yes, you.

CHIHUAHUA: *'Er . . .'*

Tell him, everybody.

DOG BRIGANDS: *'One's a windborne, the other's an emission.'*

See me afterwards, the Chihuahua. How he thinks he's going to survive on the streets, Lassie only knows. You see his little woolly coat some Two-legs has knitted for him? Woolly coats, woolly brains. You wouldn't think he's a dog. *Are* you a dog? I can't hear you. Speak up.

CHIHUAHUA: *'I'm only small.'*

Oh, you're only small! I thought you had some disease! I thought you'd not been well! What are the human-based scent groups?

CHIHUAHUA: *'I'm not sure – I'm a very small dog.'*

Come up the front. Why is your head shaped like that?

CHIHUAHUA: *'I'm only little. I'm a little fellow.'*

Right. Now you're going to stand there in front of everybody until you tell me the human-based scent groups. *Well?*

GERMAN SHEPHERD: *'Hums and fugs, Chico.'*

CHIHUAHUA: *'Hums and fugs!'*

Yes, you won't have him to look after you out there, you know. Hums and fugs. Now you go away tonight and learn your hums and fugs, or I shall get hold of you and *eat* you. Off you go. Hums and fugs. Which are which?

COCKER SPANIEL: *'Fugs are the male group and hums are the female group!'*

Very good. What's your name?

COCKER SPANIEL: *'Snooky Savage, sir!'*

Why is that?

COCKER SPANIEL: *'Because when I bite people I use a hedgecutter action and my eyes glow like two little red coals, sir!'*

   (Cheers go up.)

Good boy! Bite the good bite! I bet Snooky can tell us what the ten scent subcategories are, as well.

COCKER SPANIEL: *'Snuff, sniff, whiff, waft, savour, snort, pong, poo, phew and phaw!'*

   (Applause.)

How would you classify a rabbit carcass, Snooky?

COCKER SPANIEL: *'Well, it depends: if it's been dead three days, it would be snuzzle, subcategory pong.'*

Good dog – and what would you do with it?

COCKER SPANIEL: *'Roll in it.'*

Why would you roll in it?

COCKER SPANIEL: *'Because it contains butyric acid to enhance my sense of smell, sir!'*

Excellent nosework there from Snooky Savage. Give him another big round of applause!

(*Deafening ovation.*)

Now then . . . I'm out and about on the streets, and I'm interested in fairly recent messages – I don't want to know about messages from beyond the grave or anything like that. What can I tell about a scent from its thermal character? Black Lab?

BLACK LABRADOR: *'Whether it's a body deposit?'*

Nooo.

GINGER MONGREL: *'Its age.'*

Its *age*, right. And how do you tell a body deposit, Black Lab?

BLACK LABRADOR: *'Well, it will be either hum or fug if it's human-based, and either snuzzle or spoor if it's non-dog animal-based.'*

And if it's *dog*-based it will be –

DOG BRIGANDS (*in chorus*): *'CHUMFO!'*

And what is a *pheromone?*

DOG BRIGANDS: *'A sexual trace!'*

Right. So when I'm on the streets, looking specifically for scent pictures on the subject of female dogs, I must key on good thermal profiles of –

DOG BRIGANDS: *'Chumfo pheromones!'*

CHUMFO PHEROMONES. What *about* Chumfo pheromones? Well, it's fairly *unlikely* that

Some of them charge three chewsticks a session

you'll find on your travels a lot of *billets-doux* from sex-hungry she-dogs expressing their frenzified passions towards you. You do get the occasional one, such as 'Compliments of my season', and 'French lessons – Matty Fluff' with the number underneath, but it's a job getting the phone-box door open, and besides, you very often have to pay: some of them charge as much as three chewsticks a session. Plus, it usually happens that these kinds of messages are fairly old, and covered with a lot of salty scents from other male suitors, and by the time you reach the cutie in question, she's well past her frenzy and probably vomiting in the fireplace.

So *generally* what we are looking for are not direct invitations from she-dogs, but a subtle hint, a sign, a token, a suggestion. To the experienced nostril, practically any female message can be interpreted in terms of its pheromone content, though you often have to sift through a lot of scent garbage first, before you get to the telltale signal at the bottom (if you'll pardon the expression).

For example: *'I do not desire to meet you at the fishpond.'* Use of 'desire' in this context can only mean one thing – so get to the fishpond where all will undoubtedly be revealed!

How about this one: *'I have been feeling under the weather recently.'* This is a common hidden pheromone ploy, probably meaning that the bitch is experiencing her pre-frenzy, or even her tizzwozz, and is inviting you to mate with her very shortly. Use of the term 'under' gives the game away.

Another common one is this: *'I'll be glad when August is over, as the heat is making my ankles swell up.'* Well, you'd have to be pretty stupid to walk past *that*, wouldn't you – note the direct reference to her 'heat' and 'swelling up'.

But what about this: *'I have no pressing need to look at your garden shed.'* At first sniff, this looks like a pretty emphatic refusal, but smell more shrewdly and the close conjunction of 'pressing' and 'need' gives you the real, hot-blooded message underneath. The garden shed is the obvious 'place of assignation', so you should go there immediately, having had a wash in the fishpond.

Of course, you may not be lucky enough to find any pheromones in the message at all, despite terrific scenting efforts and the wildest interpretative flair. But don't despair! There's sure to be something hopeful. Any mention whatsoever of 'positions', 'seating arrangements', 'breath' or 'pants', 'litters' (*not* cats), or getting 'in arrears' or 'behind' with payments – these are all potentially rude and suggestive. And of course, any references, however oblique, to 'tails' or 'tailgate parties', 'backs', 'bottoms', 'heating arrangements', 'hot flushes', 'seasons', or any mention of 'ties' – family ties, club ties, bow ties, that sort of thing. Always be prepared to scent between the lines, even when umpteen rival males have been at the message before you and added ribald comments of one kind or another. Even male Chumfo, for example about upcoming events and political meetings, should be examined carefully in case it contains any passing references to bitches in the area. You never know: there might be a coded Valentine message from some rival dog to his sweetheart hidden beneath an advertisement for something else, in which case you could get there before him! Be alert at all times. And remember, *'If your nose is to the ground, Leg-overs will soon be found'*. Any questions?

RED SETTER: *'Yes: could you tell us, if we find a message from a bitch, what sort of thing to say in reply?'*

Doggerel! Every time. Females like a bit of doggerel in preference to prose – it makes them feel romantic.

RED SETTER: *'I don't know any doggerel.'*

Yes you do. Somebody tell him a bit of doggerel.

COCKER SPANIEL: *'Come into the garden, Maud,*
For the black bat, Night, has flown;
Come into the garden, Maud,
I am here at the gate alone.'

Outstanding, isn't he?

(Standing ovation.)

Chapter Six

Step Three: Seeing off Rivals

Even if you get out and about on the streets and learn to decipher Chumfo, even if you manage to locate female talent and rumpy-pumpy opportunities, you will never be a successful mater unless you have mastered the art of fighting and biting. Because even if the she-dog herself doesn't upset your concentration by trying to tear your ear off, the likelihood is that for every bitch on heat in your area there will be at least a dozen male rivals barring your way and waiting to sink their teeth in your accessories. What to do about this problem? Where to acquire the techniques to enable even a useless little dollop like Chico the Chihuahua to see off his opposition? Look no further, Brothers and Brigands.

We are extremely honoured to have with us tonight, at considerable expense, and all the way from the Far East, two exponents of the lethal art of *Foo Fang*. And they are going to demonstrate to you skills dating back to the imperial Kendoggies of ancient China and Japan, skills handed down in sworn secrecy from generation to generation of Foo Fang fighting dogs. Brothers and Brigands, will you welcome – on my left, from Soochow in China, All Chow Champion and Gold Collar Holder, Master Choo Nor Nip!

(Thunderous applause.)

And on my right, Brothers and Brigands, from Yokohama in Japan, Blackcollar Kendog Shar Pei Champion and seventh Dan, Master Dan Ding Dong!

(Deafening ovation.)

(Hushed commentary:) And as these two formidable fighters square up, I can tell you a little bit about them: first of all, Choo Nor Nip, as you see, is wearing the traditional 12-inch false fangs of the Soochow masters, feared denizens of both Foo Fang and Far Fling techniques. They harden their paws by firing them in kilns, and learn the essential discipline of pain-

control by placing their tongues beneath Sumo wrestlers who are about to sit down (hence the legendary blue tongues of these tremendous Chow dogs). Choo Nor Nip lives with his mate and four puppies, and trains on a diet of raw cats. He checks in at 58 pounds.

His opponent, seventh Dan, Dan Ding Dong, is a forepaw-poke specialist and leading exponent of the Foo Fang lethal weapon, the jugular ginlock, which we may be lucky enough to witness here tonight. His spectacular wrinkles, typical of the Shar Pei, are acquired by going up and down in fast lifts, and Dan Ding Dong weighs in at a colossal 63 pounds on a diet of pullets' gullets, lizards' gizzards and bullocks' liversausage laced with anabolic steroids. The traditional black studded collar and dewspikes signify a veteran of at least 150 fatal bouts. He lives with a French Poodle and likes discussing Zen Buddhism and polishing his kennel with former opponents.

And as they get underway, it is Dan Ding Dong who nips into the flank of his adversary there with the flying buttock bite. Choo Nor Nip responds very smartly with a gizzard chomp and back leg snap, flicking Dan Ding Dong's hind legs deftly across his loins – and yes, Dan Ding Dong is down, there, playing for time with the forepaw double eye poke and full shoulder munch. And notice the ease with which these champions carry their full fighting weight as Choo Nor Nip lifts his 63 pound opponent with his false fangs and, using the Far Fling, tosses him backwards over his shoulder, shaking him violently – but Dan Ding Dong catches the Chow's ear, yes, as he is tossed back and forth, the Shar Pei lays on the famous Yokohama gobble – and Choo Nor Nip won't enjoy that I can tell you – and he's clearly in a spot of bother there as Dan Ding Dong works away at his ear, but he retaliates nicely with a foreleg lock – and here comes the groin gnash as well, with Choo Nor Nip using those 12-inch fangs to advantage – and it seems to pay off, as Dan Ding Dong releases and goes instead for a running leg lock, circling his rival warily now – and he won't get anywhere much with that – as Choo Nor Nip goes back inside with the headmare and muzzle maul, yes, he likes this move, lowering Dan Ding Dong's head towards the canvas and trampling on it slightly – and Dan Ding Dong looks to be struggling – but no! he's up again, and coming back strongly now with the belly-bite and entrail fling, rebounding the Chow as though on a piece of elastic there, and oh my goodness me, he catches him on the snap back with a full-bore gonad dropkick, and this could be it – as we see Dan Ding Dong press home the advantage immediately with the Tokyo tail-swing – he throws – Choo Nor Nip goes down heavily – and yes, this is it – Dan Ding Dong moves in quickly and applies the jugular ginlock – and the Chow champion signals that he's in difficulties – and in fact I think he's losing consciousness – I can see his legs wiggling despondently – yes, he's lost consciousness there, altogether, and he's lying fairly doggo. And so there we have it, Brothers and Brigands – seventh Dan, Dan Ding Dong, the Kendog Shar Pei Champion from Yokohama, demonstrating there the destructive art of Foo Fang. Give him another round of applause!

(Hoots, hollers, stamps and whistles.)

Now, not all of you, obviously, can hope to achieve the level of skill we've seen demonstrated here by our guest fighters. A dog doesn't become a Foo Fang expert overnight: it take years of punishing dedication and self-sacrifice. But with regular practice and hard work, each and every one of you can add at least one of these moves to his courting arsenal. Watch. Work. Wise up. Perhaps the jugular ginlock may be *your* key to success! Practise it on rodents and frogs in your spare moments, though, before trying it out on next door's cat. Then gradually work your way up to small, elderly, crippled dogs in your area. If you yourself are small, elderly and crippled, practise assiduously on cushions and squeaky toys until you've mastered the basic technique. Put those hours in – and you, too, can turn yourself into a lethal dog like our grand masters here tonight! Well, like *one* of our grand masters – the other one's not feeling any too perky at the moment. Could some of you bear him respectfully into the yard? Thank you, brothers.

But what if you can't master Foo Fang? Are you then finished, forlorn, and four feet sticking up in the air? No. Not with the Randy Barker school of combat psychology, you're not. Let's imagine you're out on the street, and that you've located a Red Hot district, with a bitch on heat known to be in residence and male dogs cruising the kerbs craftily, hoping to pick up a pheromonal whiff. Recce the area, and home in on the she-dog's love nest. If there is a queue already forming outside, give it a miss – or you may face a two-pronged attack. Avoid silly moves, such as turning up covered in cow dung, or following humans coming out of the bitch's residence bearing her fragrance – this is a mug's game. Camp patiently outside and await developments.

Now, supposing you've done all this correctly, and you're sitting there, going over in your mind the names of famous stud dogs of our time, ready for action – and suddenly, out of the corner of your eye, you notice another male coming towards you. What do you do?

Turn and face him. Size him up. Is he bigger than you? Is he overweight? Is he long-haired (you won't want to end up getting a lot of dog hairs in your mouth)? Is he smooth-coated? Is he curly-coated? Is he wearing a Cromwell helmet and full battledress? Does he smell at all queer? Is his hair in a bow? Can you see any good holding points? There are seven key

Practise it on rodents and frogs in your spare moments

attack spots to aim for: a shocking bite or blow to any of these regions can cause your adversary to faint clean away or even drop dead in front of you. These points are: the head, the face, the ears, the neck, the chest, the belly and the goolie area. They are known in 'Bushidog' terminology as the 'Li-lo' or death spots, although your enemy may be able to hang on indefinitely if the grip is not properly applied, and agree only to a technical knockout. If the ears are chosen, remember that *both* ears must be seized, tied in a small knot, and used as a means of swinging the rival round your head and throwing him in the river.

Whichever Li-lo point you choose, you should begin your campaign with some diversionary tactics to put your enemy off his guard and give you the telling advantage of a surprise assault.

Diversionary tactics:

1. Have with you ¼ lb of boiled sweets from your 'emergency escape rations'. Wait until your rival has a few of them stuffed in his gob before making your surprise attack.
2. Feign a double or even triple limp, stumbling and falling down in the road occasionally to show you are not fully fit, and a meths drinker.
3. Lard your conversation with fruity phrases about other male dogs, and turn one forepaw slightly outwards. Pretend you know nothing about the bitch's residence, and that you are off to have a quiet fag in the churchyard.
4. Carry a pair of binoculars or a box of matches, and pretend you are preoccupied, watching local wildfowl, or trying to start a small fire.
5. Apply a modest amount of shaving cream to your lower lip and make slightly deranged, slavering noises, in order to show that, in the past, you have been in contact with a recent source of infection. Have with you a forged French passport made out to a Monsieur Pepe la Rage.

All the time, keep a watchful eye on your adversary's Li-lo points, ready to go for your all-out assault without warning. As soon as you are within range, fly at him savagely, seizing the main chance, and anything else you can get your fangs into. Wearing false fangs is *not* advisable unless you can afford to have them properly fitted. Improperly fitted false fangs may be swallowed, or cause whistling noises.

Remember that both ears must be seized

Body language

Be alert to this at all times. Any dog worth his bones will be aware of customary canine signs, signals, stares, stances, scents and sounds that betoken imminent aggression and possible flare-up situations. A dominant dog will normally 'look big' by raising his head, tail, ears and hackles, and prancing about importantly. Avoid this, to allay suspicion. Feign inferiority by lowly crouching and 'looking small', tucking your tail under, bowing your head, flattening your ears and narrowing your eyes in supplication, as if to say, 'Don't be wasting your teeth on the likes of me, your Highness.' If necessary, lie down on the footpath and show him your little pink belly. Avoid looking directly in his eyes or staring at him, as this may signal that you wish to fight, or that you are trying to hypnotize him for your own private purposes. If he mentions 'territorial rights', say that you are unable on your present salary to afford a mortgage but that you are looking forward to buying a ruined outdoor toilet in southeast Asia with other dogs on a time-share basis when your ship comes in.

Words of warning

Of course, you won't want to use submissive gestures or any such caper *if the bitch herself happens to be watching*. If you do, she may form the impression that you are a wanker, and be unwilling to allow you any favours. If you have a female onlooker like this, you will have to adopt a more dogly approach. Stand tall, swelling out your guard hairs, and chewing gum very casually. Erect your hackles and other appliances. Bark in a deep, dogly voice. Have a small shred of red mincemeat hanging out of the side of your mouth to look like the remains of a recent victim. Amble towards your rival with a dead-eyed expression, as though you are bored with all the killing, having been careful to smother your fur liberally with oil of wintergreen, or anything slippery and unappetising. Don't wait for the bell – there may not be one within earshot. Go straight in at an angle, keying on your enemy's Li-lo points and being prepared to pull out and start again if you find a particularly gristly bit. Do not attempt to use the Foo Fang 'entrail flick' unless you are very experienced. Above all, if you sense that you are on the receiving end quite a lot, try to avoid yelling out (this is where chewing gum comes in handy). Extricate yourself carefully, cock your leg on a nearby lamp-post to save face, and clear off. Come back later when your wounds have healed and try another tactic. Always try to avoid death wherever possible, as this is a great setback in mating endeavours.
  Any questions?

DOBERMANN: *(Whisper whisper.)*

I understand Hansie the Dachshund and the Yorkies have had a squabble outside, and that they wish to rejoin the group, if we have no objections. They are apparently very contrite. Very well, let them in. *Come in, come in, that's it.* Let them parade their injuries – this is typical, isn't it? While we've been in here contemplating the finer strategies of honourable combat, and watching our Foo Fang experts demonstrate their skills as an *art form*, this lot have been out the back, having an ignominious bundle over nothing, and this is the result. Look at that. Sit down, all of you, before you fall down, for the love of Lassie – I've never seen such a disgrace. Yorkies, please do *not* bring any more fatalities into my lecture theatre. Leave them outside for burial. Hansie the Dachshund, sit over the other side away from them. Look at the state of you! And blood all over my clean floorboards. Well? What have you got to say for yourself?

HANSIE THE DACHSHUND: *'Anysing to come on Erwin Rommel?'*

Chapter Seven

Step Four: The Loose Bitch — A Step in the Right Direction

Brothers and Brigands. Lusters. Lechers. Whoopie-worshippers, gropers, humpers and rumpy-pumpers. Seekers after female hide. Bonkers. Bouncers. Bangers. Frisky boys. I want to ask you a question. *What is the point?* What is the earthly point of my giving you the benefit of my years of study and research, my wide reading and vast experience, telling you all about the need for Revolution? Eh? What is the point of my sounding the clarion call, to go forth, multiply, people the world with pups, so that one day we shall outnumber the two-legged Tyrant? Do you want to hear about this takeover, this liberation, this Putsch? Of course not. Are you eager to learn about the social, the political, the religious, the philosophical ramifications of what we are doing? No. The only 'ramifications' you're interested in are lewd, rude and rumpy ones. The only 'takeover' you want to know about is how to *take* one hind leg and swing it *over* a bitch's bottom.

Very well. The Loose Bitch. Yes, the stuff of dreams. The aim and end of every right-thinking, red-blooded, pistol-packing, leg-cocking, self-abusing, self-respecting male dog who ever walked the face of the earth. I trust I have everybody's attention. We are talking red meat, here.

(Rapt silence.)

What do we mean by the term, 'loose bitch'? We mean a female dog running about without a lead on. Kindly try and focus your filthy little minds on the literal meaning of my text, please, and not go rummaging in the metaphorical underworld. Now, usually, for reasons which I have touched on in an earlier discourse, bitches in fact are locked up. So how precisely does one become loose? Well, by eating certain very rich foods, such as offal, or having a very bad fright. This is one avenue. Or by getting lost and all of a tizzy. Sometimes, owners are very careless, and allow their female dogs to stray, even when they are in season. The

How to take one hind leg and swing it over a bitch's bottom

she-dogs in question here are most likely to be Mongrels, because female Pedigrees are more expensive and more likely to be kept indoors with the family heirlooms – though they, too, may be kicked out over some trifling habit such as barking all night or peeing on the polyanthus. But there is another group of loose females of particular interest, and these are the ones who have come into season, and devised a means of getting out on the streets to be mated. These frenzied females may be very determined, driven to distraction by their bodily desires, and use every means at their disposal to rush out in a dogly direction. They will jump over perimeter fencing and six-foot walls, tunnel furiously, and employ any of the escape methods I have outlined in my section on the subject – and others they have invented themselves. One bitch I can think of now regularly tricks her owners into thinking she is just popping out for a moment to dig up worms for her squeaky toy. Once outside, she belts off in the direction of a local takeway, for what purpose I leave you to imagine (see pages 36–7).

Let us suppose, then, that we have located a loose bitch, or that she has located us. What then? Well, first of all, we must give her the time-honoured once-over, or 'butcher's hook', or *look*. This is the prerogative of all males, large or small, young or old, Pedigree or Mongrel – even if they happen to be partially sighted. Because we must each and every one of us be on the alert for bitches with lampshades over their heads, who have been cruelly blemished, deformed, or disfigured in wars, or bred to look like pterodactyls, meat loaves, apes, coconuts, stick insects or piles of elephant droppings, who are trying to palm themselves off as decent mates, and who may suddenly, in the middle of being served, whip off their lampshades to give us a heart attack. I know of several tragic cases of male dogs now undergoing analysis who have been through this distressing experience and lived to tell the tale, and who can vividly recall every detail, including the colour of the lampshade. Spare yourselves. Examine the bitch before you. Examine the bitch before you – *anything*! Take no notice of all this old twaddle about 'breed standards'. These have nothing to do with canine aesthetics and may actually be dangerous to your health. Look at the bitch and say to yourself, 'Do I fancy this, or am I doing it out of a sense of charity?' (And if you think this sounds harsh, you should listen to human males on the subject – they give their females marks out of ten.)

What do we look for in a bitch's conformation? Well, first, she should be of an acceptable age, preferably able to walk unaided. If she is blind in one eye from cataracts, or has mange, or creeping paralysis, or other frailty of this nature, it may be as well to suppress your desires, since such a bitch may, in breeding terms, throw poor stock (though if she has creeping paralysis she may not throw them very far). Look for something less decrepit: remember we are trying to build up the world's healthy dog population.

Much has been barked and written in Chumfo on the contentious subject of female beauty. Dogs have fought over the finer points for centuries, as the issue arouses very powerful feelings. The saying, 'One dog's meat is another dog's poison' has even passed from dog parlance into the human vernacular.

DOG BRIGANDS: *'Wo!'*

What exactly is female beauty? The following points will serve as a guide:

1. *Raised ankles.* A flat-footed bitch who plods about with bow legs is enough to turn any dog off his dinner. The ankle should be finely turned and not overly hairy, the nails well-worn and smooth, and not covered with nasal debris, manure etc. Mandarin toenails should be avoided.
2. *A vigorous, tripping gait.* The legs should move with a carefree, light carriage, and lift in coordinated sequence. If they cross over badly, this may indicate stifle problems, and if they all leave the ground simultaneously, the animal may well be a gazelle.
3. *An alluring hip-line.* The hip-movement should be luscious, languid, lithe, lissom, loose, li – yes, Hansie the Dachshund?

HANSIE THE DACHSHUND: *'Oh oh oh!'*

What's the matter with him?

HANSIE THE DACHSHUND: *'It's my voonds! Heff you a pain killer?'*

No. Shut up. The hips should be light, luxurious, licentious, lazy, lovely and locomotive. They should move from side to side with a wiggle rather than a wobble. Some bitches are dedicated wobblers, not through any inherent sexiness but because they are carrying excess blubber. There is nothing wrong, of course, with fat bitches, provided you are prepared to spend time ferrying tasty snacks to their residence in a wheelbarrow. Now I've lost my thread through that Hansie. Was I on 3 or 4? Ah yes.

4. *The tail.* Every dog has his own individual preferences here, and some dogs develop what we call, in psychiatric terms, a 'tail fetish' and are unable to mate with a bitch who does not possess a very long, luxuriant appendage. These dogs find it necessary, when dealing with bitches who have been docked, to bring along an appliance to attach to the female's hindquarters. These are obtainable from Doo Dog Nights Ltd, Unit 17, Back Alley Buildings, Wolverhampton: send for their free, tastefully illustrated catalogue featuring the latest 'Suki-brushes' and 'Fifi-waggles' in a range of colours and sizes.
5. *The waist.* All bitches, regardless of breed, should have a waist, and I see no reason to

spend valuable street time attempting to woo a bitch who has not bothered to maintain one. It's no good their wearing girdles, or breathing in trying to simulate the waistline effect, either, as this is particularly repulsive and may lead to flatulence.

6. *The dugs.*

(Tittering breaks out.)

Stop that. Bitches should have a minimum of six dugs – don't accept any less. If they say they are waiting for another couple to come through, I'm afraid that's just their bad luck. We have to draw the line somewhere. Six dugs are the absolute base rate for suckling a healthy litter of six pups, and there's nothing worse than a bitch going about without the requisite number. I think I've got six myself, as a matter of fact, so a female can certainly make the effort. 'Dugs', by the way, is the correct term – *not* 'nipples', 'teats' or the even more ridiculous 'titties'. Did I say something funny, the Poodle at the back? You, yes.

POODLE: *'I thought they were called "little boobies"'.*

Be quiet.

CORGI: *'Or digglies. We always call them "wiggly digglies"'.*

BLACK LABRADOR (spluttering): *'Or bitches' bibblies!'*

(More tittering.)

SHUT UP! Calm down. I've never understood this puerile obsession with the Mammary Gland. They're just functional maternity bumps for feeding puppies. So long as a bitch has got half a dozen, why worry? You're trying to get your leg over, not opening a dairy.

Right, now I should like to draw attention to this wall chart, showing the Female Urogenital System. This is the tail base, here, and we are looking at the system from the rear, as you can see. Now, in the background, behind the behind, or bottom, we have the cervix, urethra and so on, which we needn't lose a lot of sleep over, but these two apertures here at the front are very important. This one under the tail is known as the Outlet, and this lower one is known as the Inlet, or the Other. If the Outlet and Inlet or Other are the other way round, with the Other at the top beneath the tail and the other, the Outlet, under the Other, this is known as Astigmatism. If, on the other hand, the Outlet and the Other or Inlet are not in a straight vertical line, as here, we may be dealing with the Plough constellation or even Ursa Major. Mating with either of these should not be undertaken without proper medical

We always call them wiggly digglies

supervision. But if, as here, we have neither an Inlet nor an Outlet, nor any other indication of an Other, we should examine the bitch carefully in case she is actually a stuffed toy. So that's all pretty straightforward. Now, let us turn the bitch round and look at the *other* end.

Full frontal aesthetics, which we have touched on already with regard to lampshades, is both a science and an art. What a bitch looks like from the front is very important, and not only to one's digestion. The female's looks can be transmitted to her pups, as for example, when she gives them a filthy look, or a knowing look. What then should immediately strike us about a bitch's countenance? Is there an art to reading the bitch's mind in her face? What do we notice? What are we looking for? Hansie the Dachshund – what are you looking for?

HANSIE THE DACHSHUND: *'A couple of crêpe bandages vooldn't come amiss.'*

Oh, stop harping on about your ridiculous injuries. You can glue that bit back on when you get outside.

HANSIE THE DACHSHUND: *'But it's dengling on ze ground now.'*

Well, that's your fault. Take your mind off it by telling us what you look for in a bitch's full frontal appearance.

HANSIE THE DACHSHUND: *'Oh, ze usual sings. Ze little short legs; ze shiny earstyle framing ze face of an angel; ze little smile clenching ze cigarette holder in ze teese, as she sits on ze barstool singing, "See vot ze boys in ze beck room vill heff".'*

I see. Well that's one point of view. Anybody else?

GREYHOUND: *'I can tell you a very, very ancient description of greyhound beauty, if you like. It's from a hundreds of years old Chumfo message tiddled on a medieval wall.'*

Good, let's hear it.

GREYHOUND: *'Are you ready?'*

Yes, get on with it.

GREYHOUND: *'Are you set?'*

For crying out loud, tell us the sodding description.

GREYHOUND: *'You have to say GO!'*

GO!

GREYHOUND: *'The greyhound should be headed like a snake*
And necked like a drake,
Footed like a cat, tailed like a rat,
Ribbed like a beam, glossy like a bream;
The first year she should learn to feed,
The second learn to follow on a lead.'

Right. And your name is?

GREYHOUND: *'My Son. And she should have long toenails if possible, and slightly pursed lips, with a long pointy snout, long lashes, and wide grey eyes with a faraway look.'*

Well, My Son, that's very interesting. Very romantic.

GREYHOUND: *'In medieval times, you see, greyhound was spelled "gre-hounde", "gre" being the archaic term for "highborn", "fine". So greyhound meant "gentle dog", "beautiful dog".'*

Fancy. I never knew that. Isn't that interesting?

GINGER MONGREL: *'No, it's not. It's bloody terrible.'*

Oh? Why is it terrible?

GINGER MONGREL: *'Well, we don't want to know about all this old "dainty dalliance" twaddle. We want to know about Mounting, and Caper! That's what I come here for. All his lot are kept in little boxes, anyway, with bleeding flaps on the front, thinking about stuffed rabbits. I bet that's all he's ever stuffed – look at him. Long streak of piddle.'*

CORGI: *'My Son is entitled to his opinion.'*

GINGER MONGREL: *'So he's your bleeding son. And there's me thinking he was a son of a b–'*

Brother Ginger! As Mongrel Delegate you bear a heavy responsibility here tonight, representing a very large number of our honoured comrades at arms. I don't want to have you put outside like a common Pedigree. Apologize to My Son.

GINGER MONGREL: *'I thought he said he was his son.'*

Apologize.

GINGER MONGREL: *'Aw, all right. Sorry, John, you bleeding dickhead.'*

Thank you.

Chapter Eight

Step Five: Courting your Cutie

When you have located a suitable female, it is not a good idea simply to set upon her. You risk serious assault charges from the bitch, particularly if she happens to be a Foo Fang expert. Much wiser to go through the proper channels: the age-old canine ritual of wagging and whining, prancing and dancing, the nose nuzzle and the chin rest, which signal the onset of hanky-panky. Fortunately or unfortunately, canine courting customs are among the very few animal passions *not* studied in depth by human documentary makers, who take great delight in making vast programmes about lewdness in ladybirds, copulating kangaroos and all manner of humpage in between (including camels). So you are unlikely to win acclaim in David Attenborough films, though you may get the bucket-of-water award for Most Seductive Scene in a Public Place. And, since there *are* no informative documentaries on dog courtship (television companies should apply to me in writing for details, enclosing a stamped addressed envelope), many of the more isolated dogs among you may not even know the correct courting procedures. Don't be embarrassed by this! Not every canine is an instinctive Dog Giovanni.

Let us begin at the beginning, with the thrill of *the chase*, forward and reverse gears. These should be practised beforehand, on cyclists, moving vehicles and next door's cat, before trying them out on a she-dog. Practise turning your speed up and down like a gas jet, as well as swerving and cornering, as the bitch may be very cunning or a 400-metre champion. If you are on a straight chase and have steam well in hand, allow the she-dog occasionally to think she's managed to get away before overhauling her again. Then, when you finally flag her down, accuse her of exceeding the speed limit. This way she may well be too confused and fagged out to attack you.

Let us suppose, then, that you have hounded your she-dog to a standstill and that you are now in fairly close range, commanding the bitch's full attention. This is the time to launch

Skip lightly about, head up, tail held high

PRANCING 0   DANCING 1

into the next stage of your ritual: *prancing and dancing*. Skip lightly about, head up, tail held high, ears as erect as possible, circling her with a high-stepping gait and displaying your attributes (if you are without a tail, for 'tail held high' read 'backside held high' and hope for the best). Furious wagging, while it may not necessarily entrance your prospective mate, will at least fan your nether regions and ensure personal freshness. Whining is *not* obligatory. Every so often one finds a bitch who is positively put off by a whingeing male, particularly if she is an Australian Terrier and he is a Pomeranian. Others simply fall asleep at the first sign of being serenaded.

When you have circled and stamped and pranced and farted about for what you consider a decent amount of time, your next step is to *Assess the Signs*. By this I mean you must make a prudent judgement as to how your display is going over. Study the bitch's body language. Is the language bad? Does her entire demeanour seem to signal 'body bad luck'? What emotional signs do you observe in her carriage and facial expressions? Do you perceive signs of heat, frenzy, invitation, willingness, tizzwozz, compliance? Or simply signs that you have bungled? Here is a helpful guide:

When not to take no for an answer

Signs are:
1. Running away very slowly, continually looking back to check pursuit.
2. Leaving suggestive markings.
3. Marking suggestive leavings.
4. Permitting sniffing in transit.
5. Flaunting her rear end in a manner likely to be considered provocative.
6. Alluring glances, come-hither stares, boudoire stares, winking, etc.
7. Making little helpless whimpering noises.
8. Pouting, panting or steaming from the nostrils.
9. Holding her tail at an erotic angle.
10. Holding your tail at an erotic angle.
11. Pointing or gesturing towards her rump.
12. Wearing cosmetics, suspenders, lingerie etc.
13. Giving off amorous Chumfo pheromones of subcategory savour, snort, pong, poo, phew or phaw.

14. Backing into bollards, litter bins, parked car bumpers etc.
15. Backing into male dogs, panting, screaming and crying out, 'Oh for a bit of the other before I expire!'
16. Beckoning with the forepaw.

When to take no for an answer

1. 'Get lost' glances.
2. Cold-hearted expressions, such as 'Piss off out of it, you dirty dollop!'
3. Very long, sharply pointed claws reinforced with steel tips or Blakeys.
4. Sounding a rape alarm.
5. Loud, bare-gummed snarling.
6. Loud, aggressive barking, especially using a megaphone or loudhailer.
7. Carrying lumps of concrete, a Bowie knife or stun gun.
8. Covering her rear end with cowdung, dead fish or other foul-smelling substance.
9. Continuous loud farting.
10. Wearing a large Band-Aid over her orifices.

Once you have made an Assessment of the Signs, and determined that they are in your favour, you should proceed to the next step: the *Nose Nuzzle*. This is a very alluring amorous custom practised by dogs and Eskimos since time immemorial. If properly executed it achieves an atmosphere of complete trust and intimacy between yourself and the she-dog or Eskimo about to become your mate, lasting friendship, growing passion, and a union of the senses. If improperly executed it can lead to fights, disfigurement and sinus problems. Here is the correct procedure.

First, move your muzzle gently adjacent to that of your partner, at an angle of about forty-five degrees. Do this gradually, and without sudden jerks, keeping an eye out for female gum visibility (signalling the onset of snapping). Next, snorting gently to clear your airways, tenderly apply your hooter to the bitch's snout. If you have done this correctly, you will feel a little puff of warm air, and a scent cloud will envelop you, containing all the relevant information about this particular she-dog: what she had for dinner last Tuesday, whether or not she has mated before (or before last Tuesday), whether or not she has had pups, and most important of all, whether or not she charges three chewsticks. Decode these details carefully and, if the bitch seems suitable, move on to the next stage of arousal: the *Chin Rest* ploy.

After you have achieved nostril union, it is time to angle your body beside the she-dog ready for more direct physical contact. Caressing her gently to reassure her, and without dribbling on her fur, rest your chin lightly on her back and make an imperceptible wiggling movement with your lower jaw. This will convey your erotic feelings directly to the bitch's spine and arouse in her the most sensual appetites. The Chin Rest has nothing whatever to do with the appliance commonly found on violins. Yes?

BLOODHOUND: *'I'm very worried about dribbling – how does one avoid it?'*

(Murmurs of assent and concern.)

Yes; I'm glad you've asked me that, Bartleby. I get a lot of letters from dogs suffering from CRD Syndrome who have been unable or unwilling to seek veterinary help. It isn't a particularly rare condition either, though it can be an extremely worrying one. Basically, CRD or Chin Rest Dribbling Syndrome to give it its proper medical name, afflicts dogs of a sensitive nature who are anxious to please their partners and not do anything out of order. Let me read you a typical letter from my postbag, from D.D. of Grantham in Lincolnshire (D.D. I take to be an abbreviation for Dew Drops or Dribbly Draws):

> Dear Mr Barker,
> Is there a Dog Samaritans, as I am considering topping myself. I have been a CRD Syndrome sufferer for two and a half years. The onset of my illness dates back to a terribly embarrassing courting episode with a gorgeous little cross collie from the bottling yard near my home. I had been pursuing her and dreaming about mating with her for weeks, as she seemed just right for me, and after many false starts I finally succeeded in interesting her in the fishmonger's loading yard. After my prancing and dancing was well received, I proceeded to the Nose Nuzzle, but became so exhilarated and carried away that I lost all control of my feelings and began to drool on the little she-dog's neck. At this her attitude towards me seemed to change and she became angry and irritable, saying she had just finished moulting and had a new coat. I apologized profusely but was seen off in some disgrace. Since then, I have been unable to attempt the Chin Rest with other partners, for fear of my affliction being discovered. Is there any government aid for CRD Syndrome sufferers?

(Sniffling noises among the audience.)

Sadly, it's a familiar story, and no, there is no government aid. This particular letter-writer obviously has the condition to a marked degree, because he mentions symptoms appearing at the Nose Nuzzle stage, as well as during Chin Rest, when it normally occurs. Other sufferers write in a similar vein, asking if I know of a medical breakthrough. I must be perfectly frank: there is as yet *no* complete cure for CRD Syndrome. So-called 'miracle discoveries' you may hear of, such as 'Doggie Gum Glue' and seal suction devices for holding the lips together, are in fact perfectly useless and may lead to death by starvation. There are, however, several courses of treatment available and simple remedies based on common sense which have proven helpful to sufferers and which I can recommend. These should at least be tried before suicide is undertaken.

CRD Syndrome remedies

1. First, avoid mating with bitches who are extremely attractive. CRD Syndrome is triggered by unusual levels of arousal, and in laydog's terms, if you are not aroused, you will not drool. Seek instead to mate with bitches you find fairly repulsive.
2. Avoid mating in very hot weather, in greenhouses, deserts, boiler rooms etc.
3. Have in your mouth two small pieces of gauze or absorbent cotton wool, lodged in the folds of your lower lips and resting against your gums. If the bitch queries this, say you have recently undergone dental scaling, or that you are understudying Marlon Brando's part in *The Godfather* (or Lassie's part in *The Dogfather).*
4. *Before* resting your chin on the bitch's back during courting, stand to one side, with your forelegs slightly spread and head lowered, and allow your mouth to drain out on the ground, spitting several times. Try to avoid hoiking or noisily clearing your throat, as the bitch may take this to be a sign of lung disease. If you are a St Bernard, use your little brandy barrel as a spittoon (most St Bernards do this anyway).
5. If you really can't avoid drooling, take with you a duster or chamois leather to discreetly wipe the bitch's fur before she notices anything amiss.

Never make the mistake of taking the she-dog into your confidence and saying, during seduction, 'By the way, did you know I am a CRD Syndrome sufferer?' Unless she is a trained psychotherapist she is unlikely to be helpful, and may run off and hide in the coal cellar.

Leaving aside CRD Syndrome, however, let us suppose that your Chin Rest ploy *has* gone smoothly – what then? Well, you will usually find by this stage that the she-dog is showing signs of excitement and extreme arousal. Unfortunately, some bitches at this point suddenly react very strongly against their own bodily desires, as though confused or disturbed by them. These females normally fall into three categories: A) the 'Wild Bitch' – one who invites attention only in order to get within striking distance; B) the 'Tease' – one who invites attention only to keep running off to examine trivialities, small soil displacements, dead insects etc.; and C) the 'Sit Down Bore' – one who invites attention and then parks her behind, saying she's suddenly had a migraine attack. Unless you are prepared to spend a good deal of time delving into the complex reasons for their foolishness, such bitches should be avoided.

The last part of the courtship ritual is to position yourself for the final assault. This is known, in the language of canine sex therapists, as *Getting Behind Her Satan*, and I was hoping at this point to introduce a guest speaker to tell you how it is done, but he said he was a bit behind schedule and recommended the following tips be conveyed on his behalf:

Things to remember (copyright Satan the Rottweiler):

1. Make sure you know which end is the rear (this is where the Nose Nuzzle can be a useful precaution). *Never* ask a very long-haired she-dog which end is her face, as she may become quite shirty.
2. Do not fall down on the job. If you feel you are about to faint, try to go off somewhere privately and do it in a secluded spot.
3. Do not break the spell of your wooing techniques by proclaiming loudly, 'I'm going round the back now, darling.'
4. If you are about to mate in the back of a car, steady yourself beforehand by pushing your hind feet into an old pair of rubber gloves.
5. If you are a member of a small breed, do not attempt to scramble or climb up a bitch's rear by using a wooden crate or step-ladder. The bitch will almost certainly be put off, especially in the event of an accident.

GEOFFREY THE YORKIE (1): *'Oh 'eck! So* that's *where I were oop a goom tree wi' Golden Retriever!'*

Finally, brothers, if you have followed all these instructions correctly, and if you have engineered yourself into the optimum position behind the bitch's rump – congratulations! You are now ready for Mounting!

GEOFFREY THE YORKIE (1): *'Doos 'e mean like roody greyhound Mick the Miller in t' Nutural 'Istory Museum?'*

GEOFFREY THE YORKIE (2): *'Noo – that's stoofin. Mountin's different to stoofin.'*

GEOFFREY THE YORKIE (1): *'Oh aye. I were wrong there, then, an all.'*

Make sure you know which end is the rear

Chapter Nine

Step Six: 'I will arise and go now, and go to Innisfree'

What actually happens during mating? No dog knows. Many believe you actually leave your body for a time, and go up in the air. There have been many Chumfo reports of 'out of the body' experiences, and of dogs seeing their bodies mating as though from a great height. (Some have become so exasperated that they have actually barked at themselves.) Other theorists reason that you simply get so excited during the Sex Act that you *think* you've gone up in the air. While you are holding onto the female with your forelegs and bobbing up and down, you tend to forget where you are. All you can see of the she-dog is the scruff of her neck and the top of her head, so she could be anybody, really. You are virtually all alone, staring in front of you at nothing, concerned with your own mounting feelings to the exclusion of everything else in the universe.

And what are you thinking about at this time? Well, some unfortunate dogs who write to my agony column think about the possibility of their brains coming to pieces and exploding in all directions with bangs and whizzes. This is not always pleasurable, and a few of the afflicted turn aside from pursuing she-dogs altogether and become what we call 'inhibited'. Most dogs, though, think about flying. It is quite acceptable to think about flying; about sailing, soaring and swooping down like a seagull, and gliding back up again on the updraughts and thermals. Others feel as though they are on a trampoline, bouncing and springing up very high, so that they actually rise above the clouds and the stars. One famous Mongrel, the prophet Eyesore, had a vision in which he bounced right up into another world, and saw a big white Bearded Collie reclining on a golden beanbed, with a golden bone and a golden waterbowl, and lots of little cherub Papillons with wing-ears fluttering back and forth, ministering unto him. Eyesore was 'sore dumbstruck and afraid, wherefore he uttered not', but hung in mid-air for several seconds staring at the spectacle with his eyes out on stalks, before plummeting back down again. *Alleluya.*

Eyesore was 'sore dumbstruck and afraid'

DOG BRIGANDS: *'Alleluya!'*

All these flying experiences (though not so much the exploding brain one) are accompanied by a feeling of delirious lightness and joy, as though a dog could bark out in a huge great voice, 'Look at me! I'm flying! I'm a wonderful boy!' or recite appropriate lines of human doggerel such as 'I will arise and go now, and go to Innisfree'. And while all this is going on in the mind, something equally joyous and miraculous is going on in the body.

Millions and trillions of tiny, titchy little tadpoles, smaller than newborn baby fleas, which have been waiting patiently inside the male organs, are preparing to make their death-defying journey into the she-dog's body, swimming on the voyage of their very lives up the drainpipe and out of the end with a woosh! Their one ambition is to enter a female egg, which is like a very small glob of jelly to look at, and join with it at the Point of Organism, to make puppies be born. This is known as 'fertilization'.

GINGER MONGREL: *'As in compost?'*

GEOFFREY THE YORKIE (1): *'Do the little tadpoles do booterfly stroke?'*

(Pregnant pause.)

I'm sorry – am I speaking in a foreign language? Hello? Are you receiving me? *'As in compost'*. *'Do the little tadpoles do booterfly stroke'*. No – *they do doggie paddle*. Is anyone out there listening to me at all? Am I failing to make myself *plain?* Do you find me *despotic* perhaps? Or *dogmatic?* Is that it? You find me a little teensy bit dogmatic for your tastes? What's the problem – hmmm? What seems to be our little difficulty? *Don't you have any reverence for Nature at all? Are you all as heedless and brainless about Nature as human beings?* I despair at times. I don't have to give these lectures to make a living, you know! I could be off giving sex-therapy sessions to rich confused poofta dogs in California! Here I am, trying to convey to you something of the *wonder*, the *dignity*, the *eternal mystery* of two dogs mating, and you sit there looking at me with poltroonish, slovenly, bulbous-eyed, smirking, silly faces like a set of gormless morons, thinking up what *imbecilic, oafish, vulgar* question to ask me next, wasting my brains and my time, demeaning yourselves and demeaning our race! Right then – *if that's what you want, that suits me just fine!*

(Randy Barker collects up his papers and storms out, followed by his Henchdogs.)

* * *

CHICO THE CHIHUAHUA: *'Oo-er!'*

SNOOKY SAVAGE: *'You've done it now, Brother Ginger.'*

GINGER MONGREL: *'Wasn't me – it was him!'*

GERMAN SHEPHERD: *'It was both of you.'*

HANSIE THE DACHSHUND: *'Vill he come beck, do you sink?'*

BLOODHOUND: *'I reckon he's gone for good this time. I'm afraid we've got his dander up.'*

CORGI: *'Yes – he won't keep taking all this impertinence. He is Randy Barker, after all.'*

GEOFFREY THE YORKIE (1): *'Aw, shooroop. 'E weren't oop t' subject. "Mekin' poopies be born." Eck as like – I noo more about it meseln!'*

GEOFFREY THE YORKIE (2): *'Aye – tha'st fathered a few poops oop in Pontefract, Geoffrey, and no mistake!'*

GEOFFREY THE YORKIE (3): *'Aye – 'e 'as that!'*

DOBERMANN: *'Then perhaps Brother Geoffrey would care to continue the lecture for us.'*

GEOFFREY THE YORKIE (1): *'Well, it's dead simple, entit – shall I stand oop 'ere on this box so you can all see me? Ow's that? Got me in t' picture?'*

DOG BRIGANDS: *'Aye.'*

GEOFFREY THE YORKIE (1): *'Well as I say, matin's a simple tusk. All it is, besickally, is a matter of gettin' 'old of t' female an' dooin' this' (gestures) 'an' when thee feelst theeseln gooin' "Ooo", there's a blindin' flash, an' that's it, really. Anoother five or six little tearaways, all sturdy an' strappin' an' yellin' out for t' milk.'*

BORDER COLLIE: *'Yes, but what happens at the actual moment of conception?'*

GEOFFREY THE YORKIE (1): *'Ow the 'ell do I noo? I may be small, boot I'm not that flippin' tiddly to get down into t' tube to see what's doin' am I?'*

DOBERMANN: *'I think you're a very ignorant little dog.'*

YORKIES: *'Ere! Watch theeseln!'*

DOBERMANN: *'Well, if you know all about mating, what's a "tie"?'*

GEOFFREY THE YORKIE (1): *'What's a what?'*

DOBERMANN: *'After the male and female have mated, their bodies are joined together for up to half an hour in what is known as a "tie". What's a "tie"?'*

GEOFFREY THE YORKIE: *'Well, it's when two dogs coom first, entit!'* (Ribald chuckling of Yorkies.)

BLOODHOUND: *'This is worrying. The best thing is if one of us goes and apologizes to Mr Barker.'*

POODLE: *'Yes, we agree.'*

GERMAN SHEPHERD: *'Brother Ginger, you go.'*

GINGER MONGREL: *'Me? Leave it out, John!'*

GERMAN SHEPHERD: *'Well, you're a Mongrel. He thinks Mongrels are the blessed master race.'*

HANSIE THE DACHSHUND: *'I sink ze Yorkies should go!'*
YORKIES: *'Flamin' 'ell fire! 'E's askin' for it again!'*
DOBERMANN: *'I agree with Hansie. What say the rest of the Brothers? All those in favour of the Yorkies petitioning Mr Barker say Aye!'*
BRIGANDS: *'Aye.'*
DOBERMANN: *'All those against? Jolly good, motion carried. Off you go then, Yorkshire brethren.'*
YORKIES (going out): *'Typical, entit? Always pick on t' littlest. Aye, an' me a father at the age of woon.'*

(The door shuts very quickly behind them.)

BLOODHOUND: *'I was a bit worried by what brother Dante the Dobermann was saying there about "ties". What actually is a "tie"?'*
BORDER COLLIE: *'Because of the unusual physiology of our sexual organs, after ejaculation the male remains inflated like a bulb inside the female's body for up to half an hour. No dog knows why this should be. In the meantime, all the male can do is to dismount carefully, putting his front feet on the ground beside his mate, and what usually happens is that he turns round to face in the opposite direction, so that male and female are rump to rump. They then have to wait in that position, relaxing, while Nature takes her course and allows the male dog to free himself.'*
CHICO THE CHIHUAHUA: *'Oo-er!'*
GERMAN SHEPHERD: *'Are you happy now, Bartleby?'*
BLOODHOUND: *'Well no, I'm never happy. I think this is all very worrying, personally. All this business about "out-of-the-body experiences". I can't say I've ever had anything like that. It's a worrying business. You see, I looked up "ecstasy" in my Master's dictionary while he was away, and you know what it means? "A state of temporary mental alienation or exalted feeling" from the Greek for "standing outside"! I don't want to stand outside of my body. Supposing you couldn't get back in! Would you be dead, in that case?'*
GINGER MONGREL: *'It's nothing to worry about, Brother B! I've done it lots of times and I'm still as frisky as ever. You don't want to let it worry you. I tell you what worries me, and that's trying to think what to say to the little lady when you've mated with her, and you're stuck together for half an hour! That can be very dodgy! Because if you're not careful, she starts giving you the old grievous bodily harm of the ear 'ole about being "in love for ever more" and setting up house on the building site. You have to think of something to take her mind off it!'*
BLACK LABRADOR: *'Like what, though?'*
GINGER MONGREL: *'Well, I always tell them, "Look love, a long term relationship is only possible*

in an ideal wild, after the planet comes under proper canine control. All we can hope for under human occupation is to live from day to day, and have a fling while we can." That usually sorts them out.'

POODLE: *'But what about the puppies?'*

GINGER MONGREL: *'They're not your problem. Raising young is down to females. That's their job. You just have to clear off a mite sharpish when nesting's mentioned. And avoid giving a blood sample.'*

BLOODHOUND: *'Oh dear. This all sounds very heartless.'*

GINGER MONGREL: *'Don't be daft. You have to look after yourself. I've always been on the streets, me. You have to survive, don't you? You have to maintain your independence and spread your genes about.'*

BLOODHOUND: *'But what about your home, and your Master?'*

GINGER MONGREL: *'Never had one.'*

BLOODHOUND: *'Never had a Master?'*

GINGER MONGREL: *'Nope. Always been on my own. That's what I'm used to. Managing from day to day. You can't be tied to one partner all your life. That would be worse than being chained up by humankind – or in my case, human unkind.'*

GERMAN SHEPHERD: *'Wolves mate for life, Brother Ginger.'*

GINGER MONGREL: *'No they bloody don't.'*

GERMAN SHEPHERD: *'Yes they do – my ancestors were wolves.'*

GINGER MONGREL: *'All our ancestors were wolves. It says so in the Natural History Museum.'*

POODLE: *'Oh, here he goes again – the Wild Boy of Borneo.'*

GINGER MONGREL: *'We're all descended from wolves!'*

POODLE: *'Well, I'm not!'*

DOBERMANN: *'Yes you are!'*

CHICO THE CHIHUAHUA: *'Nor me neither!'*

SNOOKY SAVAGE: *'Sshh! Look out – the Leader's coming back!'*

PEKINGESE: *'I'm descended from people belonging to Queen Victoria!'*

BRIGANDS: *'Shut up! Sshhhhh!'*

(The door is flung open. Randy Barker, very grand, marches back into the room, followed by his Henchdogs and, at a respectful distance, the Yorkshire Terriers. Randy Barker places his papers on the lectern and surveys his audience imperiously.)

So you all have Mounting sorted out, now, have you?

BRIGANDS: *'Yes sir.'*

And nobody has any questions?

BRIGANDS: *'No, sir.'*

BLOODHOUND: *'Well, I have one – it's about "ecstasy", sir. Apparently it means "standing outside". What happens when you're "standing outside"?'*

You hear a soppy little Yorkshire Terrier going, 'E's not oop t' subject' and 'Matin's a simple tusk'. How do I know that, Brother Geoffrey?

GEOFFREY THE YORKIE: *'Because you were standin' outside, sir'.*

Because I were standin' outside, sir. And what are you, Brother Geoffrey?

GEOFFREY THE YORKIE: *'Reet foolish, sir.'*

Reet foolish, sir. Thank Lassie these lectures are nearly finished. They're doing my brain in. Yorkie waterbowl detail, *tenshun!* Yorkie waterbowl detail, *by the left, quick march! Hup two three four, hup two three four – come on, come on, get those hairy legs up!*

Chapter Ten

Being a Gay Dog

No dog is 100 per cent male. Even the most macho among us has little dugs stuck on his chest by Nature for some purpose she has as yet failed to disclose, and a few tragic males have actually been forced by their human oppressors to undergo a surgical procedure which we shan't mention here, but which has the effect of rendering them one or two apples short of a barrel. It is not their fault, any more than having little dugs is our fault, and they should not be persecuted (well, not all that much).

There are other members of the canine community who are not what we would properly call 'male' or 'all there' in physical terms. Bitches, for example (though some may develop quite formidable qualities). Dogs whose gonads have failed to descend from higher regions. Dogs who bark with high-pitched voices after being seriously injured in fights. Dogs who, because of veterinary interference or for some other reason, lack the necessary amount of male hormones. All these unfortunates deserve our sympathy. They have been cruelly deprived of that most precious and inestimable of gifts in the natural world – masculinity.

But there is another group of so-called dogs who do not come up to scratch with regard to the masculine virtues, and who cannot be relied on to follow any of the instructions I have so painstakingly set out for you in my mounting manual. Not for them the joys of mating and multiplying! Not for them the sacred responsibility of stocking up the world's dog population. The Revolution, when it comes, will owe nothing whatever to these individuals.

One of them has come here tonight, to talk to you and answer any questions you may have about his proclivities. I thought it best for you to get the information straight from the Iron Hoof's mouth, as it were. What do I mean by Iron Hoof, Chico the Chihuahua?

CHICO THE CHIHUAHUA: *'Poof, sir!'*

Very good.

CHICO THE CHIHUAHUA: *'Nancy dog. Queer dog. Mary Ann Airedale.'*

Yes, thank you, Chico.

CHICO THE CHIHUAHUA: *'Doggie bag. Botty bandit. Warp and woof.'*

That'll do, Chico.

CHICO THE CHIHUAHUA: *'Bent boy. Weirdie dog. Little Fanny Faggot.'*

Will you shut up!

CHICO THE CHIHUAHUA: *'Yes, sir. Sorry sir.'*

It would be difficult for a dog of my own sexual integrity to speak knowledgeably on behalf of a group that chooses to opt out of the mating system and founder in a biological backwater. I have a very large waste bucket full of letters addressed to my confidential advisory service which begin, 'Dear Randy Barker, I am very depressed about being gay. Can you come over and cheer me up?' and although I am willing to give advice to the genuinely contrite and confused, I do *not* take kindly to having to fight my way through Gay Dog Rights marches in the High Street as I go about my normal and natural mating duties in the neighbourhood. Now then. This guest speaker, a Mr Pinky Pervice, is an Afghan from Abridge, and the author of several Chumfo tracts on sexual tolerance, including *The Dog Fancier in Society* and *The Deviant Dog*. He recently won the Jimmy Riddle Prize for Literature. So let me introduce Mr Pinky Pervice, and let him get on with it. Pinky Pervice!

(Polite applause.)

PINKY PERVICE: *'Hallo lovely dogs!'*

DOG BRIGANDS: *'Hallo, Pinky Pervice!'*

Come and stand under this big light bulb so everybody can keep an eye on you.

PINKY PERVICE: *'Rightie ho – he's lovely, isn't he, that Mr Barker! I adore a dog with a sense of humour, don't you? Do you like this colour? I always think pink is right for this sort of earstyle, though I'm a natural strawberry blond, but it's only a semi-permanent tint and contains no peroxide which is harmful to the hair – don't you find? Let me know if it gets too much for you, darlings. How are you – all right? Look at that dear little one with all the naughty names – isn't he just perfect? It's all right – I know you mean it! I'm just going to give you a little talk tonight, so don't all fall asleep or you'll get me into trouble! Could somebody let me*

Fighting through Gay Dog Rights marches

*borrow a tiny drop of water in case I get a little hoarse, don't misunderstand me. Have you
got a little dish there, darling? Look at him, isn't he gorgeous? I'm absolutely in mourning for
a flowery dish I used to have at the breeder's but this will do at a pinch, don't misunderstand
me. Thank you, darling – what's your name?'*
REGGIE RUFFIN: *'Reggie Ruffin'.*
PINKY PERVICE: *'Reggie Ruffin! I thought that was a pop star, darling – and I bet you're a Border
Collie, aren't you? Yes, I knew it! I'm a Border Afghan. Can you put it there, sweetheart, so
I can get to it if I need to wet my whistle, don't misunderstand me. Right, now, the little talk
I'm going to give you is entitled "The Contribution of Gay Dogs to Literature", and if you don't
know a thing about Gay Dog Literature, don't worry one iota, because it's very accessible and
easy to enjoy, and I'm going to start you off by giving you just a tiny taste, a little soupçon,
of some of my absolute favourite pieces from the Gay Doggerel Anthology, just to get you going,
and this first one I've chosen because it's one that might actually be familiar to some of you
and I think it's my absolute personal favourite. It's by Wee Willie Winklesworthy, who was one
of the famous Lakeland Terrier Poets, and I've chosen a stanza from "The Labradors":*

> *I wandered lonely as a Peke*
> *That preens and prances out of doors,*
> *When all at once I saw a clique,*
> *A host of Golden Labradors,*
> *Beside the lake, beneath the trees,*
> *Cocking their legs upon the breeze.*

(Noisy clearing of throats.)

*And then Winklesworthy goes on to tell how he beheld the Labradors tinkling "as the stars
that shine" and how this ravishing vision returns to him in tranquillity when he's resting on
his sofa "in poncive mood". And then his mind leaps away with him to the joyous realization
that "A poet could not but be gay in such a canine company." That's one I can really
recommend.*

*Now this next one I've chosen for you is called "Ode to the Westie, Rose", and it's by one of
the great Romantics, Percy Basenji Shelti, who died at an early age in a hairdressing accident,
and I think it's my absolute favourite. "Ode to the Westie, Rose":*

> *And, like a rabid lurcher, lean and pale,*
> *Who totters forth, wrapped in a gaudy towel,*

> *Out of her kennel, led by the insane*
> *And drunken wanderings of her feeble brain,*
> *The Westie, Rose, arose and gave a burp,*
> *The white and shapeless twirp.*

Which, I think you'll agree with me, conveys something of the very essence of poetic imagery and one can actually feel the effect on the senses. Now, this last one I've selected because of its very personal nature, and I think this has to be my absolute favourite. It's by the great Irish Setter and Dog of Letters, O'Cur Fido O'Faggoty Wilful Wild Dog, and it was written in the County Dog Pound, where he was languishing for several years, cruelly imprisoned for straying from the straight and narrow and camping out. It recalls the great love of his life, Boysie the Borzoi, with whom he had the most tender dealings.

> *Yet each dog kills the things he loves*
> *And puts him in the bin;*
> *Some do it with a poison bone,*
> *Some with a jagged tin.*
> *The coward does it with a lick,*
> *The brave dog with a grin.*

Which, I hope you'll agree with me, gives at least a glimpse of some of the richness to be found in this absolute treasury of Gay Dog Verse. Now, I'd like to go on, if I may, to explore with you a few of the jewels to be found in Chumfo prose, where gay dogs have been singularly active. One only has to point to classics like Three Dogs in a Boat, The Tale of Two Setters, Pointer Counter Pointer, Chow Green was my Valet, and Tess and the Dobermanns, to realize what a contribution they have made, to say nothing of the drama, and masterpieces such as Lab's Labours Lost, and The Taming of the Shi Tzu, as well as more contemporary works like The Dog's House – yes, darling?'

Is this going to go on much longer?

PINKY PERVICE: *'Well, I'm fairly easy, darling – why, do you think they're tiring?'*

I think they might want to ask you a few questions before the close: we all have to leave here very shortly.

PINKY PERVICE: *'Ooh – fire away, boys! Ask me absolutely anything you like. Yes – is that little*

Reggie Ruffin with his paw up?'
REGGIE RUFFIN: *'Does a Poet have to be gay?'*
PINKY PERVICE: *'Well, it's not absolutely essential, but it's difficult to see how you'd have the sensitivity without, darling. The finer feelings, if you follow. You see, all dogs have in their nature a masculine side and a feminine side, and if you neglect and crush the feminine aspect, you become brutal and harsh, and ashamed of your own deep emotions. In other words you become what we call "butch".'*
BUTCH THE BOXER: *'I'm called "Butch"!'*
PINKY PERVICE: *'Yes, and I don't suppose you'll be writing "Paradise Lost" for us, will you, duckie!'*
SNOOKY SAVAGE: *'Are you saying John Milton was gay?'*
PINKY PERVICE: *'No, I should think he was pretty miserable, what with being blind and everything.'*
DANTE THE DOBERMANN: *'Do you get a local government grant for giving these talks?'*
PINKY PERVICE: *'Only a tiny little one – hardly enough to keep me in hairsprays, sweetheart.'*
GEOFFREY THE YORKIE (1): *'Is it true that gay dogs like theeseln 'uv doon a bit of spyin'? For t' Rooshians an' that?'*
PINKY PERVICE: *'Well, we've all been responsible for the odd little leak.'*
BARTLEBY THE BLOODHOUND: *'Do you suffer from CRD Syndrome?'*
PINKY PERVICE: *'I shall ignore that question as hostile, bigoted and unhip, and just the sort of bitchy thing one learns to expect from Bloodhounds, who were originally bred for rounding up fugitive slaves.'*
CHICO THE CHIHUAHUA: *'Do you have a doggie bag?'*
PINKY PERVICE: *'No, and you're a naughty, narrow-minded little devil!'*

Right, I think that's all we have time for, Brothers and Brigands.

REGGIE RUFFIN: *'Is that your own hair?'*
CHICO THE CHIHUAHUA: *'Have you ever been pregnant?'*
PINKY PERVICE: *'I blame your mothers! Look at you – no manners, no culture, no finer feelings whatsoever. You're all brutal, cynical and cruel!'*

Brothers and Brigands, Pinky Pervice – give him a big round of applause!

PINKY PERVICE: *'Self-satisfied little monsters! You're just like human beings! You're vulgarians, priding yourselves on your sexual prowess, going forth to breed a new generation of vulgarians! "Revolution." What do you know about oppression in the first place, that's what I'd like to know!'*

A DEAD LETTER TREE

The odd little leak

Right, thank you so much for being with us tonight!

PINKY PERVICE: *'You don't know you're born, some of you! That's right – manhandle me! This is what I've come to expect. Persecution at the paws of guttersnipes and Philistines!'*

Help him out into the yard, there, that's right, brothers.

(Pinky Pervice is carried out, screaming and raving.)

Hansie the Dachshund, you're very quiet – are you all right? We don't seem to have heard from you recently.

HANSIE THE DACHSHUND *(in a very high-pitched voice)*: *'No, sir – my voonds vere troubling me, but I feel a lot better now.'*

Jolly good – is there anything we can get you? A drink of water perhaps?

HANSIE THE DACHSHUND: *'I'd love vun of zose little doggie bags to put my sings in!'*

Chapter Eleven

The March of the New Dawn

Brothers and Brigands, you have listened all night to the golden words of Randy Barker. You have learned all about the sexual revolution. Now, a new dawn is rising, a dawn unlike any other dawn – the Dawn of the Dog! And this Canine Awakening will herald in the start of a new era, one in which dogs will walk tall, stand erect, mount up, arise, and throw off their leads for ever. We are emerging from the long night of human oppression, the long night of abuse. We have spent that night getting to grips with ourselves, preparing our hearts and minds for the task ahead. We have learned watchwords and slogans – 'Bite the Good Bite', 'Out and About', 'Freedom from Cuts'. And I will give you another: 'Strength Through Sex.' By 'Sex' we do not simply mean Copulation. We mean Population. We mean Confederation. We mean Emancipation. We mean Revolution. Bark it in barns. Bark it from the rooftops. Bark it beside still waters. The Canine Uprising is upon us. Armed with this knowledge, and an unshakeable belief in our natural instincts, we who were deformed and downcast are about to be reformed and recast! We who were divided are about to go forth and multiply, and build a new world for our puppies, and our puppies' puppies, and our puppies' puppies' puppies – yes? What *is* it?

REGGIE RUFFIN: *'Shouldn't Hansie be going to the vet's?'*

Vets? Aaghh! *Thaee! Thaee! I spit on that word as an abomination. I anathematize that word. Wash your mouth out, that dog! No, Hansie will not be going to the vet's.* Because vets, Reggie Ruffin, are the men in the white coats. Vets have been one of the prongs in the three-pronged attack against us, in the very forefront and vanguard of the Human struggle to overwhelm us. They have used a vast scientific and medical arsenal, including chemical weapons, to keep us in a state of submission and subservience to the Human Way. They nobble and neuter us. They nip in between us and our natural instincts. They 'cure' us of piddling indoors to attract proper mates by Chumfo messages. They 'cure' us of the wanderlust to go out and look for them. They 'cure' us of aggression, by which sole means we may hope to defend ourselves from human tyranny in the home. And worst of all, unless we are Pedigree stud dogs, they use every means in their power to 'cure' us of our normal sexuality and 'cure' our females of bearing our puppies. So no, Hansie will not be going to the vet's. He will not be chemically or surgically 'cured'. He will heal up according to Nature's law of survival of the fittest, or he will die.

BRIGANDS: *'Fffffff!'*

HANSIE THE DACHSHUND: *'Gott in Himmel.'*

I spoke just now of a three-pronged attack. Hopefully, as we in this room go forth this morning in freedom and pride, *we* shall never meet these enemies again, but all dogs should be on the alert for them, nevertheless. So I shall give you all the Three Bewares.

1. Beware vets

If you should be taken for any reason to a veterinarian's waiting room, do not co-operate. When your turn comes to be led into the surgery, squat on your hindquarters and refuse to budge. Pull back and try to duck your head out of your collar. If all else fails, hook your hind leg round the doorpost and lever yourself back out of the room. Employ all your fighting arts to the full. Resist physical examination. Bob and weave to avoid this. Wiggle your buttocks to avoid the thermometer. Fidget to prevent injections, and, if necessary, bite the vet on the behind as he turns to fill the syringe. If he attempts to administer drugs by putting pills or potions in your mouth, clamp your jaws together. If he manages to get pills inside, spit them out on the floor and trample on them. Do not swallow anything. Fight against their chemical weapons with all your strength. Do not allow the vet to give you an anaesthetic. Run wild in the surgery upsetting his equipment. If he succeeds in injecting you, resist drowsiness by barking, howling or playing very loud music on a ghetto blaster. Dance about to keep your brain active. Punch bag, skip, or do windsprints to fight off tiredness. If, however, you simply cannot stay awake, and are forced to undergo a surgical procedure, upon regaining consciousness, examine your gonad area carefully and make an accurate assessment of the damage. Pull off any bandages or plaster with your teeth and undo stitches to see if things can be mended. If they can't, do not allow being neutered to deter you from mounting. Many neutered dogs continue randy as before, and although they may not actually be able to sire any more pups,

Do not co-operate

they can still put up a jolly good show, and lead a full and active sex life. Send for my booklet 'Neutered Dogs and Their Desires' (price 40p, available in brown paper bag). Remember: Vets may tether our tadpoles, but they cannot undermine our urges! There *is* life after neutering!

2. Beware breeders

If you are a Pedigree, wash your paws of their puppy sausage factories for ever. Say 'no' to breed standards and dog deformity. Resist all attempts by breeders to force you to mate against your wishes, or with bitches you consider unsuitable. Turn vicious and intractable. Run riot at shows, mounting all and sundry, including those impertinent little charlatans called judges. Better still, take the first available opportunity to escape from the kennels altogether, and become a dog about town.

3. Beware headshrinkers

This new but growing army of animal psychiatrists are attempting to alter your behaviour. Don't let them! Do not allow yourself to be hypnotized, or sent to the booby hatch. Do not permit your brain to be washed or your head to be shrunk. Refuse to have it immersed in water. Ignore their high-pitched whistles and rape-alarms. Close your ears to the cunning counselling and their endeavours to implant new behaviour patterns in your mind. Keep concentrating and focusing your thoughts on the Revolution, dog rights and dog pride. Recite over and over to yourself, 'I will mount and I will mate. I will serve Nature, not you. I will obey my instincts, not you. I will go out and about, and breed with bitches of my choosing. I will do as Randy Barker says, I will do as Randy Barker says, I will do as Randy Barker says (repeat this several times). I will be guided by his teaching, for he will lead me to the Promised Land, and there will I lay me down and have a little drink of water.' *Alleluya!*

Brothers and Brigands, outside, daybreak is at paw. Soon I shall ask one of you to push off the light switch and then, with my loyal Henchdogs, I shall lead you forth through the yard and onto the streets, to form the first phalanx of dog freedom fighters, marching to glory, calling our brother and sister dogs to the Revolution as we go. But first I want to close this meeting by asking you all to place a forepaw on the dog beside you, and to sing with me *'The Mongrel Aire'* (No. 141 in the *Dog Hymnal).* Are you ready? Then strike up, Brigand Band!

Run riot at shows mounting all and sundry

BRIGANDS:

> *Oh Mongrel dog, oh Mongrel dog!*
> *We march at daybreak, all agog.*
> *No leads or collars rein us in;*
> *We've chucked our choke chains in the bin!*
> *Now on we march, and up we flog,*
> *To mounting glory, Mongrel dog!*

(The brigands continue humming softly the refrain of 'The Mongrel Aire'.)

And so, Brothers and Brigands, in the name of Nature, we are now going forth onto the streets to begin the Uprising. Forward we shall go, not to be turned aside by human wiles or temptations of kindness, by fear, or cruelty, starvation or despair, choosing freedom, freedom at any price. *Are we ready to march to glory, brothers? Are we ready to begin our new lives? Are we ready to found a new world? RIGHT THEN. FORWARD. FOLLOW ME.* Yes, Brother Hansie?

HANSIE THE DACHSHUND: *'I sink I vill just pop home and let my mistress look at my voonds.'*

POP HOME? Do my ears deceive me? She'll take you straight to the *vet.* Have you been listening to anything I was saying a moment ago, about the Three Bewares? *Pop home?* For the love of Lassie. Can you believe this, Brothers? He wants to *pop home!*

BARTLEBY THE BLOODHOUND: *'Well, I'd better, as well, actually: I'm awfully worried I may have left a nice shank bone under the sofa.'*

GEOFFREY THE YORKIE (1): *'Aye, me an' all – I've t' watch cricket on t'telly: it's England v. West Indies!'*

I cannot believe this. Is anybody else thinking of 'popping home'? What about the rest of my army – are you all solidly behind the Revolution? Dante the Dobermann – I appoint you my lieutenant.

DANTE THE DOBERMANN: *'I'd better not. I have to go back. I'm sorry, Master.'*

Reggie Ruffin – What about you?

REGGIE RUFFIN: *'Well, I left a small flock on top field, sir.'*

Is *nobody* joining the March of the New Dawn?

GINGER MONGREL: *'I am, great Leader. I'm coming with you!'*

SNOOKY SAVAGE: *'And me, sir. I'll only get put down anyway if I go home.'*

What about my Henchdogs? Well?

HENCHDOGS: *'Er – we have to get back to the guard-dog agency, you see.'*

So this is it, is it? This is where it all ends. The hope, the glory, the bunting, the bitches hanging out of the windows as we go by, with tails aloft, marching to end centuries of cruelty. I might have known. All great leaders come to this, eventually, I suppose. We all meet our *assassins*, our *pisspots*, on the way to posterity. Very well. Come on then, Brother Ginger and Brother Snooky. We're off to the publishers with these manuscripts. This will become a standard work, you mark my words. A classic, like *Mein Kampf* and *Das Kapital*. We'll show them. We'll proclaim the message worldwide. Absolutely world bloody wide. Off we go then. Can one of you push off the light switch? Last one out close the door, and mind the corpses as you go through the yard.

CHICO THE CHIHUAHUA: *'I'm coming with you, sir!'*

No, you're not.

CHICO THE CHIHUAHUA: *'No, I am!'*

Clear off.

CHICO THE CHIHUAHUA: *'Listen – Chumfo, snuzzles, spoors, air-omas, kemapoos . . .'*

(They go out.)

Champion Star Stud Bang Boy, who dropped dead on the job